An Introduction to
Electrical Circuit Theory

An Introduction to
Electrical Circuit Theory

G. Williams

Lecturer in Electrical Engineering
School of Applied Sciences
University of Sussex

First edition 1973
Reprinted 1975 (with corrections), 1977, 1979

Published by
THE MACMILLAN PRESS LTD
London and Basingstoke
Associated companies in Delhi Dublin
Hong Kong Johannesburg Lagos Melbourne
New York Singapore and Tokyo

ISBN 0 333 14194 6

Printed by J. W. Arrowsmith Ltd, Bristol, England

Contents

Preface

Many textbooks owe their origins to undergraduate lecture courses; this book had its beginnings in a lecture course in engineering science given by the author at the University of Sussex. When the course was begun several years ago the familiar problem of not being able to recommend a single, inexpensive, book to the students taking the course was encountered. The nature of the course structure at Sussex with its major and minor subjects made the problem more difficult because the students attending the course included not only electrical and electronic engineers but undergraduates from many other scientific disciplines too. Educational experiments in the presentation of course material being conducted at the time also meant that printed lecture notes were prepared for the course and it is with these that this book had its beginnings.

While the course contained much circuit theory other topics were included which do not appear here and conversely this book contains several topics not covered in the course. The additional material has been included so that the book may be considered to be an introduction to the subject of circuit theory viewed as a separate discipline and not viewed as a service subject to other disciplines.

The philosophy governing the presentation of the material is that all the circuit laws, methods of analysis and circuit theorems are developed using the simplest possible circuits containing only resistances and d.c. sources. Thus the discussion is not clouded by the examination of the more complicated circuit elements and sources which introduce time variations; the intention is for the student to master the analytical techniques before he goes on to apply them to the more complicated circuits. Application of the techniques to frequency domain circuits is then a logical step which allows the student to concentrate on the frequency domain concepts.

The background knowledge of readers is assumed to be school mathematics and physics but to include no circuit theory. It is also assumed that students will be covering such topics as complex numbers, second-order differential equations and linear algebra simultaneously with their studies of circuit theory and such mathematical topics are not discussed in detail here.

I would like to acknowledge the advice, co-operation and support I have received from my colleagues at the University of Sussex. It is also no cliché to say that this book could not have been created without the active assistance, tolerant understanding and unflagging encouragement of my wife.

Many of the problems in this book were originally devised by me for Preliminary Year examinations of the University of Sussex and I am grateful to the University of Sussex for permitting me to use them.

G. W.

1

Basic Definitions
and Circuit Laws

1.1   Units and dimensions

It may be shown that all *quantities* required in mechanics may be expressed in terms of three basic physical quantities. Although many sets of three quantities may be used as the basic one, the most natural, and the one most universally used is that of mass, length and time. In the SI (Système Internationale d'Unités) system of units the fundamental *units* associated with the basic physical quantities are the metre, kilogram and second which are defined respectively in terms of the wavelength of the radiation of the orange line of krypton 86; the mass of a particular block of platinum located at Sèvres in France; and the period of oscillation of the caesium atom. All other mechanical quantities may be expressed in terms of the three basic quantities raised to various powers, which may be positive or negative, and which are termed the *dimensions* of the derived quantity. For example, force is defined in terms of the acceleration imparted to a given mass and hence the dimensional equations are

$$[\text{force}] = [\text{mass}] [\text{acceleration}]$$

$$= [M]\left[\frac{L}{T^2}\right]$$

$$= [MLT^{-2}]$$

and the dimensions of force may be written as

$$[1, 1, -2]$$

The study of electrical phenomena, illumination and systems involving heat flow require additional basic quantities and fundamental units. The additional basic quantities of the SI are electric current, luminous intensity and temperature and the additional fundamental units are the ampere, the candela and the Kelvin.

1.1.1   Electrical quantities

The fourth fundamental unit of the SI is the *ampere*, symbol A, which is now defined in terms of its magnetic effect as 'the intensity of a constant current which, when maintained in two parallel straight conductors of infinite length and negligible

1

cross-section placed at a distance of one metre apart in vacuo, produces between them a force of 2×10^{-7} newton per metre length'.

The unit of current may be defined in other ways with reference to other physical effects associated with it. An earlier definition was concerned with electrolysis, or the chemical effect of current, and referred to the amount of silver deposited by passing a current through a solution of silver nitrate. Other possibilities include the heating effect associated with current flowing in conductors; a definition based upon energy; and the force exerted by charged particles at rest. All other electrical quantities may be defined with reference to their physical effects in terms of the basic quantities of mass, length, time and current and again the powers to which the basic quantities are raised to obtain the desired quantity are termed the dimensions of the quantity. Some of the definitions of electrical quantities follow.

Electric charge, symbol Q. The ultimate unit of charge is the electron which has a mass of approximately 9.1×10^{-31} kg and possesses a negative charge. An electric current consists of a flow of electric charge through a conducting region and hence the integral of current with respect to time is charge. The unit of charge is the *coulomb*, which is defined as the charge transferred by a current of one ampere in one second. Conversely, the ampere may be defined as the flow of one coulomb of charge through a cross-section in one second. Hence

$$i = \frac{\mathrm{d}q}{\mathrm{d}t}$$

and the dimensions of charge are

$$[Q] = [TI]$$

Potential difference, symbol V. The unit of potential difference is the *volt*, symbol V, and it is defined in terms of energy. The flow of an electric charge may have associated with it a transfer of energy and therefore when a charge is moved from one point to another the electric potential difference existing between those points may be defined in terms of the energy required to move the charge. The volt is that electric potential difference existing between two points if a charge of one coulomb receives or delivers one joule of energy in moving between them.

The dimensions of energy are

$$[ML^2 T^{-2}]$$

and the dimensions of potential difference are therefore

$$[V] = \frac{[W]}{[Q]}$$
$$= \frac{[ML^2 T^{-2}]}{[TI]}$$

Hence

$$[V] = [ML^2 T^{-3} I^{-1}]$$

Electric power, symbol P. It follows from the definition of potential difference that if charge is continuously transported from one point to another, through a potential difference, energy is continuously transferred. As power is the rate of doing work, the power associated with the transportation of charge is given by the product of voltage and current. Instantaneously

$$p = \frac{dw}{dt} \frac{\text{joules}}{\text{second}}$$

but

$$v = \frac{dw}{dq} \cdot \frac{\text{joules}}{\text{coulomb}}$$

and

$$i = \frac{dq}{dt} \frac{\text{coulombs}}{\text{second}}$$

hence

$$p = \frac{dw}{dt} = \frac{dw}{dq} \frac{dq}{dt} = vi \text{ watts}$$

The total energy is therefore

$$w = \int p \, dt = \int vi \, dt \text{ joules}$$

1.1.2 Dimensional analysis

The technique of dimensional analysis is a powerful tool for checking the results of analysis and calculation. It may also be used to deduce the form of an equation describing a physical phenomenon. The technique is based upon the necessity for every term in an analytical equation to have the same dimensions.

As an example, consider an electric circuit consisting of a resistance and an inductance in series connected to a time varying electric potential. The application of Kirchhoff's voltage law (see later) results in the equation

$$v = Ri + L \frac{di}{dt}$$

The principle of dimensional homogeneity demands that the two terms on the right-hand side of the equation must have the dimensions of voltage. The dimensions of resistance are

$$[ML^2 T^{-3} I^{-2}]$$

and hence the dimensions of (Ri) are

$$[Ri] = [ML^2 T^{-3} I^{-2}] [I]$$
$$= [ML^2 T^{-3} I^{-1}]$$

which are the dimensions of electric potential. Similarly the dimensions of $[L(di/dt)]$ are

$$\left[L \frac{di}{dt} \right] = [ML^2 T^{-2} I^{-2}] \left[\frac{I}{T} \right]$$
$$= [ML^2 T^{-3} I^{-1}]$$

which again are the dimensions of electric potential.

1.2   The circuit element of resistance

Physical electrical circuits consist of interconnected sets of components such as resistors, capacitors, switches, etc., many of which are non-linear devices, that is there is not a linear relationship between the current passing through them and the potential difference existing across them. Exact analysis of such circuits is therefore, at best, extremely difficult. In order to facilitate approximate analysis of such a practical circuit the practical components may be represented by ideal circuit elements, or models, which have linear characteristics. The analysis of the ideal circuit then created is the essence of circuit theory.

There are three basic circuit components and hence three basic linear circuit elements which together with the two types of electrical sources form the building blocks of circuit theory. The elements are split into two camps; those which dissipate energy and those which store it. In the latter camp is the *inductance*, which stores energy by virtue of a current passing through it, and the *capacitance*, which stores energy by virtue of a voltage existing across it. The third element, the *resistance*, is the only one of the three which dissipates electrical energy. The two sources may also be defined in terms of energy because a *current source* is able to supply a given number of coulombs of charge per second irrespective of the energy involved whilst a *voltage source* is able to supply charge at a given energy irrespective of the amount of charge involved.

Physical resistors, which include such devices as electric fire elements, light bulb filaments, cables, etc., are generally non-linear devices. It is therefore necessary to separate the physical devices both from the idealised circuit model by which they may be represented and from the physical properties which they possess.

The physical explanation of current flow in conductors is concerned with the passage of free electrons through the lattice structure of the material of the conductor. This interpretation considers that a metallic conductor, such as copper, consists of a lattice of atoms whose outer electrons are only loosely bound to the atom. These are the so-called 'free' electrons and at normal room temperatures they are able to detach themselves and drift randomly through the lattice structure. Under the influence of an externally applied electric field the free electrons tend to drift in the direction of the field and hence a current flows. The velocity of the free electrons through the conductor is usually quite low.

Consider a copper conductor of diameter 0.25 cm carrying a current of one ampere.

Density of free electrons in copper = $5 \times 10^{28}/m^3$
Number of electrons/coulomb = 6×10^{18}

Therefore, the velocity of electrons

$$= \frac{6 \times 10^{18}}{5 \times 10^{28}} \times \frac{4}{(0.25 \times 10^{-2})^2 \pi}$$
$$= 2.4 \times 10^{-5} \, m\,s^{-1}$$

As the free electrons drift through the lattice structure they collide with the lattice atoms and lose some of the kinetic energy they have gained under the influence of the externally applied electric field. Hence there is a 'resistance' to their motion. The energy lost in the collisions is usually converted into heat.

Most materials are able to conduct electricity to a greater or lesser extent and they may be divided into three broad classes:

Conductors, such as metallic elements, which conduct electricity easily;
Insulators, such as wood or glass, which are very poor conductors of electricity as they have very few free electrons;
Semi-conductors, such as germanium or silicon.

1.2.1 Ohm's law

In 1826 Georg Simon Ohm discovered that a metallic conductor maintained at a fixed temperature will pass a current directly proportional to the applied voltage. This volt–ampere relationship known as Ohm's Law is now taken as both the definition of the electrical property of resistance and as the definition of the ideal resistance element. For the ideal resistance element

$$v = Ri \tag{1.1}$$

where v is the voltage across the element in volts, i is the current through the element in amperes and 'R' is defined as the *resistance* of the element in *ohms*, symbol Ω.

The law may be quoted in an alternative form as

$$i = Gv$$

where G is the inverse of resistance and is termed the *conductance* of the element in *siemens*, symbol S.

The electron theory of metallic conduction may be used to explain Ohm's law.

Consider that the conduction electrons in the metal structure have a mean random velocity $\bar{c}$ and a mean free path λ for collisions between the electrons and the atoms of the lattice structure.

The time t between collisions is then

$$t = \frac{\lambda}{\bar{c}}$$

A voltage applied to the metal will set up an electric field within the metal and as the electrons are negatively charged they will tend to drift in the opposite direction to the electric field. The force on the electrons is $F = Ee$ where E is the electric field and e is the charge on the electron. Hence the electron experiences an acceleration for a time t and its maximum velocity will be

$$c_{max} = \frac{Eet}{m}$$

where m is the mass of the electron.

The mean drift velocity which is superimposed on the random velocities of the electrons is half this value, that is

$$c_{mean} = \frac{Ee}{m} \times \frac{t}{2}$$

and therefore

$$c_{\text{mean}} = \frac{Ee}{m} \times \frac{\lambda}{2\bar{c}}$$

If there are n conduction electrons per unit volume of the metal then the current density J is

$$J = nec_{\text{mean}} \frac{\text{amperes}}{\text{metre}^2}$$

and

$$J = \frac{nEe^2\lambda}{2m\bar{c}}$$

A small element of the metal of length l and cross-sectional area A will then have flowing through it a current of

$$I = JA$$

The potential difference across the element is

$$V = -El$$

The potential difference/current relationship is then

$$V = \left(-\frac{2m\bar{c}}{ne^2\lambda} \times \frac{l}{A}\right) \times I \qquad (1.2)$$

which is seen to be similar to Ohm's law.

The *resistivity* of a metal is defined as the resistance of a unit cube of metal between opposite faces and hence from equation (1.2)

$$\text{resistivity} = \frac{2m\bar{c}}{ne^2\lambda} \text{ ohm metre}$$

The symbol for resistance and the sign convention adopted for it are shown in fig. 1.1. It is seen that when a current flows in the resistance the terminal at

Figure 1.1   Symbol for the resistance element

which the current enters is considered positive to the terminal from which the current leaves.

It should be noted that the direction of current flow is opposite to the flow of the negatively charged electrons which constitute it.

1.2.2 Non-linear resistors

When a current is passed through a resistor, energy is dissipated by the resistor, its temperature increases and its resistance increases. Thus the current in a resistor will not, in general, be directly proportional to the applied voltage and it will usually fall with temperature. The resistor is thus non-linear. Many practical resistors exhibit this property; an illustration is shown in fig. 1.2 which shows a typical resistance-current curve for a tungsten-filament lamp.

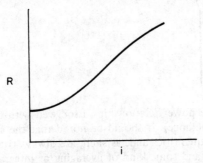

Figure 1.2   Typical resistance–current characteristic of a tungsten-filament lamp

Several devices have been developed which have enhanced non-linear properties which are useful in instrumentation and control circuitry. One of these is the 'thermistor' which is made from a special semiconducting material similar to ceramic oxide. The unusual property of this device is that its resistance remains relatively constant with temperature until a critical temperature is reached, after which the device has a very high temperature–resistance coefficient. Thus, if the device is placed in series with and in direct physical contact with, say, the windings of an electric motor, when the temperature of the motor exceeds some permissible limit the thermistor increases its resistance and cuts off the supply to the motor.

1.2.3 Power dissipated by resistors

Consider a resistance which has a current i flowing through it and a voltage v existing across it as shown in fig. 1.1. It has been shown that a system which has an instantaneous voltage of v across it and an instantaneous current of i flowing through it has an instantaneous electrical power of p associated with it where

$p = vi$ watts

Thus the electrical power dissipated by resistance of fig. 1.1 is

$p = vi$

The characteristic equation for a resistance is

$v = Ri$

or

$i = Gv$

Hence,

$$p = i^2 R \quad \text{watts}$$

or

$$p = v^2 G \quad \text{watts}$$

or

$$p = \frac{v^2}{R} \quad \text{watts}$$ \hfill (1.3)

or

$$p = \frac{i^2}{G} \quad \text{watts}$$

Equations (1.3) are the power relationships associated with the circuit element of resistance (or conductance). It should be noted that the above relationships refer to *instantaneous* quantities and, as such, are always true. If the current and voltage vary with time and some kind of averaging or integrating process is carried out then power relationships for the resistance differing from the above may be obtained.

1.3   Kirchhoff's laws

1.3.1   Sign conventions

Before going on to discuss the electric circuit laws it is necessary first to adopt sign conventions with regard to the currents and voltages existing in a circuit. Electric circuits consist essentially of two types of elements; sources, which supply electrical energy, and passive elements which either store or dissipate energy. In order that the sign assigned to the flow of electrical energy shall have any meaning, a consistent system must be adopted with regard to current and voltage.

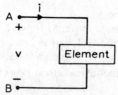

Figure 1.3   Sign conventions for current and voltage

It has been shown that a current flowing in a conductor consists of a flow of charge. The charge may be either positive or negative and therefore two choices exist for assigning a sign to the current. The usual convention is that a positive current consists of a flow of positive charge in the direction in which the positive current is flowing. The sign convention adopted for currents flowing in electric circuits is that an arrow is drawn on the circuit which designates a reference direction for the current, as shown in fig. 1.3. If a current consisting of positive charge flows in the direction of the arrow it is then said to be positive. Conversely, if a current consisting of positive charge flows in the opposite direction to the arrow it is said to be negative. Thus the arrow is an arbitrarily chosen reference direction and the actual current associated with it can be either positive or negative.

Voltage does not possess a direction in the way that current does, but it does possess polarity because as shown in the original definition it is a measure of the work done in moving a charge from one point to another and the work may be done on *or* by the charge. The convention adopted is that a pair of signs, plus and minus, are used at the terminals of an element to give a reference polarity to the voltage; the convention is that a plus sign for the voltage is assigned to the terminal where the current enters the element. Thus in fig. 1.3 A is regarded as the positive terminal and B as the negative. If the actual voltage existing in the circuit is of the same polarity as the reference signs it is then said to be positive and conversely if the actual voltage has a polarity the reverse of the reference signs it is said to be negative. Thus the signs are for algebraic reference only.

With this convention positive energy is energy supplied *to* an element and negative energy is energy supplied *by* an element. Similarly positive power is power dissipated and negative power is power generated.

A further way of expressing the convention with regard to voltage is to examine the rise or fall of potential through the element in the direction in which the current flows. If the potential falls in the direction of current flow (for example, a resistance) then the voltage is said to be positive but if the potential rises in the direction of current flow (for example, a voltage source) then the voltage is said to be negative.

1.3.2   Ideal circuit elements

Resistance and conductance
The sign convention for the resistance or conductance element is shown in fig. 1.4.

The power dissipated in the resistance is

$$p = vi = i^2 R$$

or

$$p = vi = v^2 G$$

and is positive.

Figure 1.4   Symbol for the ideal resistance or conductance element

Ideal voltage source
A constant voltage source is an ideal source element capable of supplying any current at a given voltage. The voltage across the terminals of the source is constant and independent of the current supplied. For example, if the terminals are connected together the source will supply an infinite current. The symbol for a

voltage source and the sign convention are shown in fig. 1.5. It should be noted that if the current flow is reversed (that is, the current flows *out* of the top terminal) then the top terminal will carry the negative reference sign and the bottom terminal the positive sign. The source voltage then has the opposite polarity to the reference signs and the source voltage is regarded as being negative (that is, $v = -V$).

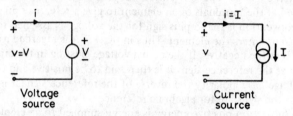

Voltage source

Current source

Figure 1.5   Symbols and sign conventions for the ideal voltage and current sources

Ideal current source

A constant current source is an ideal source element capable of supplying any voltage at a given current. The current supplied by the source is constant and independent of the voltage at the source terminals. For example, if the terminals are left open and unconnected to any circuit the source will supply an infinite voltage. The symbol for a current source is shown in fig. 1.5.

1.3.3   Current law

Kirchhoff's current law relates to the currents associated with any junction in a network where two or more circuit elements are connected together. Such a junction is termed a *node*. As a consequence of the principle of the conservation of charge and because the junction cannot store charge any charge flowing into the

(a)   (b)

Figure 1.6   Illustrations of Kirchhoff's current law

junction must immediately flow out again. Thus, in terms of currents, the sum of the currents entering the node must equal the sum of the currents leaving the node. If, arbitrarily, the currents entering the node are regarded as being positive and those leaving as being negative the algebraic sum of the currents at the node must be zero, which may be stated mathematically as

$$\Sigma i = 0$$

The current law is therefore

'the algebraic sum of the currents associated with any node at any instant is zero'.

Two examples are shown in fig. 1.6.

For fig. 1.6 (a)

$$i_1 - i_2 - i_3 + i_4 - i_5 = 0$$

or

$$i_1 + i_4 = i_2 + i_3 + i_5$$

For figure 1.6 (b)

$$-i_1 - i_2 - i_3 = 0$$

or

$$i_1 + i_2 + i_3 = 0$$

This last equation does not contravene the principle of the conservation of charge because the arrows indicate only the *assumed* direction of the currents and, of course, some of the currents will actually be positive (that is, they enter the node).

1.3.4   Voltage law

Kirchhoff's voltage law relates to the potential differences existing around any closed path within a circuit and it is a result of the application of the principle of the conservation of energy. If a closed path within a circuit is considered then the total work done in taking a unit charge around the closed path must be zero. This

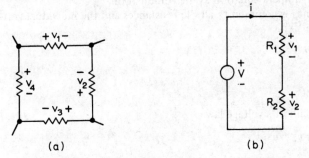

(a)   (b)

Figure 1.7   Illustrations of Kirchhoff's voltage law

follows from the conservation of energy because the energy gained or lost by a unit charge as it moves from one point to another is independent of the path between the points. As voltage is a measure of the energy gained or lost by a unit charge the algebraic sum of the voltages around any closed path must be zero, which may be stated mathematically as

$$\Sigma v = 0$$

The voltage law is therefore

'the algebraic sum of the voltages around any closed path within a circuit at any instant is zero'.

Two examples are shown in fig. 1.7.

For fig. 1.7 (a), passing clockwise around the circuit,

$$v_1 - v_2 + v_3 - v_4 = 0$$

For fig. 1.7 (b), passing clockwise around the circuit

$$v_1 + v_2 - V = 0$$

or

$$V = v_1 + v_2$$

1.3.5   Applications of Kirchhoff's laws

Resistances in series

Circuit elements are said to be in a *series* combination if they are connected together 'nose-to-tail' to form a single chain between two terminals. Thus the three resistances shown in fig. 1.8 are connected in series and it is required to find the

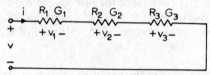

Figure 1.8   Resistances in series

effective resistance between the two terminals of the series combination. In other words, it is necessary to determine a single equivalent resistance which will have the same volt–ampere equation as the combination.

The current i is common to all the resistances and the individual volt-ampere equations are

$$v_1 = R_1 i$$

$$v_2 = R_2 i$$

$$v_3 = R_3 i$$

but from Kirchhoff's voltage law

$$v = v_1 + v_2 + v_3$$

therefore

$$v = i(R_1 + R_2 + R_3)$$

But for the equivalent resistance

$$v = iR_{eq}$$

therefore

$$R_{eq} = R_1 + R_2 + R_3$$

In terms of conductance

$$G_1 = \frac{1}{R_1}, \qquad G_2 = \frac{1}{R_2}, \qquad G_3 = \frac{1}{R_3}$$

therefore

$$\frac{1}{G_{eq}} = \frac{1}{G_1} + \frac{1}{G_2} + \frac{1}{G_3} + \frac{1}{G_4}$$

Conductances in parallel

Circuit elements are said to be in a *parallel* combination if each element is connected directly to two common terminals. A group of three conductances connected in parallel is shown in fig. 1.9. Again it is required to determine the value of a single conductance which will be equivalent to the parallel combination.

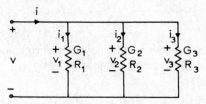

Figure 1.9   Conductances in parallel

The voltage v is common to all of the conductances hence the individual volt-ampere equations are

$$i_1 = G_1 v, \qquad i_2 = G_2 v, \qquad i_3 = G_3 v$$

and the equivalent conductance is

$$i = G_{eq} v$$

but from the application of Kirchhoff's current law

$$i = i_1 + i_2 + i_3$$

therefore

$$G_{eq} = G_1 + G_2 + G_3$$

In terms of resistance

$$\frac{1}{R_{eq}} = \frac{1}{R_1} + \frac{1}{R_2} + \frac{1}{R_3}$$

Worked example 1.1

Determine the resistance between points a and b of the circuit shown in fig. 1.10.

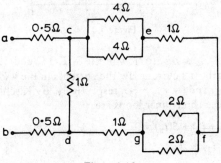

Figure 1.10

Between nodes f and g are two $2 \, \Omega$ resistances in parallel. Replace them by an equivalent resistance R_{fg}. Therefore

$$\frac{1}{R_{fg}} = \frac{1}{2} + \frac{1}{2} = \frac{2}{2}$$

and

$$R_{fg} = 1 \, \Omega$$

The circuit to the right of nodes e and d now consists of three $1 \, \Omega$ resistances in series and their combined effective resistance is

$$R_{ed} = 1 + 1 + 1 = 3 \, \Omega$$

The circuit between nodes c and e consists of two $4 \, \Omega$ resistances in parallel which may be replaced by their equivalent resistance of a $2 \, \Omega$ resistance.

Thus between nodes c and d there is now a parallel combination of a $1 \, \Omega$ resistance and a $5 \, \Omega$ resistance. The equivalent resistance of this combination is R_{cd}, and

$$\frac{1}{R_{cd}} = \frac{1}{1} + \frac{1}{5} = \frac{6}{5}$$

$$R_{cd} = \frac{5}{6} \, \Omega$$

The circuit between nodes a and b now consists of a $1 \, \Omega$ resistance in series with a $5/6 \, \Omega$ resistance and thus

$$R_{ab} = 1 + 5/6 = 11/6 \, \Omega$$

Worked example 1.2
Determine the currents in all the resistances shown in fig. 1.11.

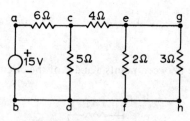

Figure 1.11

Ascribe the currents i_1, i_2 and i_3 to flow in the $3 \, \Omega$, $2 \, \Omega$ and 5Ω resistances respectively. By Kirchhoff's current law the currents in the $4 \, \Omega$ and $6 \, \Omega$ resistances are then $(i_1 + i_2)$ and $(i_1 + i_2 + i_3)$, respectively. By Kirchhoff's voltage law the voltages around the three inner loops are

$$-15 + 6(i_1 + i_2 + i_3) + 5(i_3) = 0$$

$$-5(i_3) + 4(i_1 + i_2) + 2(i_2) = 0$$

$$-2i_2 + 3i_1 = 0$$

Re-arranging these three equations gives

$$6i_1 + 6i_2 + 11i_3 - 15 = 0$$

$$4i_1 + 6i_2 - 5i_3 = 0$$

$$3i_1 - 2i_2 = 0$$

There are thus three simultaneous equations containing three unknowns and the three currents may be determined.

Potential dividers

Consider the circuit shown in fig. 1.7(b) where it is required to determine v_1 and v_2 as functions of V. The application of Kirchhoff's voltage law yields

$$V = v_1 + v_2$$

but

$$v_1 = iR_1 \quad \text{and} \quad v_2 = iR_2 \tag{1.4}$$

therefore

$$V = i(R_1 + R_2)$$

Substituting for i in equation 1.4 gives

$$v_1 = V\frac{R_1}{R_1 + R_2} \quad \text{and} \quad v_2 = V\frac{R_2}{R_1 + R_2}$$

Thus the voltage across any resistance element in a series combination of resistances has the same ratio to the total voltage across the combination as the resistance element has to the total resistance of the combination. A combination of series resistances thus divides the total potential across them according to their individual resistances.

Current dividers

Consider the circuit shown in fig. 1.9 where it is required to determine i_1, i_2 and i_3 as functions of i. The application of Kirchhoff's current law gives

$$i = i_1 + i_2 + i_3$$

and the individual volt–ampere equations for the three conductances are

$$i_1 = G_1 v, \quad i_2 = G_2 v \quad \text{and} \quad i_3 = G_3 v \tag{1.5}$$

Therefore

$$i = v(G_1 + G_2 + G_3)$$

and substituting for v in equations 1.5 gives

$$i_1 = i\frac{G_1}{G_1 + G_2 + G_3}, \quad i_2 = i\frac{G_2}{G_1 + G_2 + G_3} \quad \text{and} \quad i_3 = i\frac{G_3}{G_1 + G_2 + G_3}$$

Thus the current passing through any conductance in a parallel combination of conductances has the same ratio to the total current passing through the combination as the conductance element has to the total conductance of the combination. A combination of parallel conductances thus divides the total current passing through them according to their individual conductances.

Problems

1.1 Determine the dimensions of the following quantities:

(a) conductivity, (b) permittivity, (c) magnetic flux.

1.2   The accelerating potential V necessary to give an electron of mass m and charge e a path of radius of curvature r in a magnetic field of flux density B is given by the expression

$$V = \frac{B^2 r^2 e}{2m}$$

Show that the expression is dimensionally valid.

1.3   The starter motor of a car is connected to the 12 V battery via two copper conductors of length 1.2 m and effective cross-sectional area of 1 cm². If the current needed to start the car is 500 A determine (a) the power loss in the conductors, (b) the potential at the starter motor, (c) the power supplied to the motor, (d) the power supplied by the battery. The resistivity of copper is 1.7×10^{-8} Ω m.

1.4   It is required to produce a circuit of effective resistance 1.4 Ω by the use of several 1 Ω resistances in a series–parallel combination. What is the minimum number of 1 Ω resistances needed and how are they interconnected?

1.5   Three resistances of value 2, 3 and 4 Ω are connected in series to an 18 V source. What is the potential across the 3 Ω resistance? What is the power dissipated by the 4 Ω resistance?

1.6   Three resistances of value 2, 4 and 8 Ω are connected in parallel to a 7 A source. What is the current passing through the 4 Ω resistance? What is the power dissipated by the 2 Ω resistance? What is the source voltage?

1.7   Twelve wires, each of 1 Ω resistance, are joined together as shown in fig. 1.12.

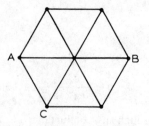

Figure 1.12

(a) Determine the effective resistance of the circuit between points A and B; and
(b) determine the effective resistance of the circuit between points A and C.

1.8   Twelve wires, each of 1 Ω resistance, are joined together in the form of a cube as shown in fig. 1.13. Determine the effective resistance of the network between points A and B and between points A and C.

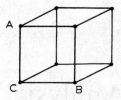

Figure 1.13

1.9   Figure 1.14 represents a street of five houses supplied at both ends by an electricity sub-station of output voltage 240 V. The distance between the houses is 50 m and that between the end houses and the sub-stations is 100 m. The cables

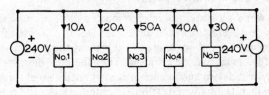

Figure 1.14

connecting the houses to the sub-stations are 1 cm^2 in cross-sectional area and have a resistivity of 2.0×10^{-8} Ω m. The current supplied to each house is: no. 1–10 A; no. 2–20 A; no. 3–50 A; no. 4–40 A; no. 5–30 A. Determine the current supplied by each of the sub-stations and the supply voltage at each house.

1.10   Show that the source potential of the circuit shown in fig. 1.15 is independent of the value of the resistance R.

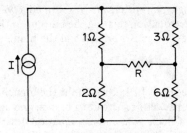

Figure 1.15

2

Methods of Analysis
and Network Theorems

2.1 Terminology and network topology

An electrical network is a system of interconnected ideal circuit elements which is
a model of a physical system or set of actual devices. In the case of resistors, the
ideal circuit element of resistance is used to represent the physical resistor in order
that analysis of the device may be achieved. Thus the ideal circuit element is a
model of the physical device and as such it is a 'lumped element' representing a
physical device which is usually a distributed system. Hence the resistance of a
conductor is quoted as a single figure but the conductor itself may be many kilo-
metres long and the 'resistance' will be distributed along its length.

The ideal circuit element is a two, or more, terminal element but the connections
between the element and its terminals are considered to be ideal resistanceless
conductors. When two elements are joined together the connection between their
terminals is assumed to be resistanceless and to be able to pass currents without
absorbing power; a *short-circuit* is then said to exist between the terminals.
Conversely if there is no connection between terminals an *open-circuit* is said to
exist between them.

An element, or combination of elements and sources, which is connected to the
rest of a network by a single pair of terminals is termed a *branch* and a branch is
completely defined by the equation relating the current to the voltage at its
terminals. Thus a single resistance is a branch and the branch volt–ampere
equation is

$$v = iR$$

which states all that is needed to be known about the branch. A series–parallel
combination of elements may also constitute a branch and again, as shown in
chapter 1 for resistances, a single volt–ampere equation describes the operation of
the branch. The junction points between branches are termed *nodes* which are considered to be resistanceless and infinitesimal. Closed paths within networks formed
by two or more branches are termed *loops*.

Thus in fig. 1.11 the 2, 3, 4 and 5 Ω resistances are branches and so is the
combined 15 V source and 6 Ω resistance. There are only three nodes as the points
b, d, f and h are common and so are e and g. The three nodes are at d, c and e and
the paths acdb, cefd and eghf are all loops.

18

The object of network analysis is to determine the magnitudes of all the voltages and currents existing in a network when the form of the network is known. The voltages and currents are therefore the unknown variables of the network and if the network contains b branches, since each branch contains at least one element and has therefore two unknown variables associated with it, there will be $2b$ unknown variables. The theory of equations states that in order to solve for $2b$ unknown variables $2b$ independent equations linking the unknown variables are required. Equations suitable for use include the branch **volt–ampere equations** and the equations resulting from the application of Kirchhoff's current and voltage laws to the nodes and loops of the network. But not all of these equations may be independent and it is necessary to apply the theory of algebraic topology to determine the number of independent equations.

As an example consider the circuit shown in fig. 2.1 where it is desired to determine all the currents flowing in the circuit.

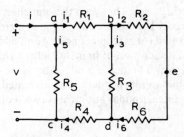

Figure 2.1   Illustration of independent nodes and loops

The Kirchhoff current equations at the nodes are:

node a	$i = i_1 + i_5$	(i)
node b	$i_1 = i_2 + i_3$	(ii)
node c	$i = i_4 + i_5$	(iii)
node d	$i_4 = i_6 + i_3$	(iv)
node e	$i_2 = i_6$	(v)

and every node appears to contribute an independent equation. But equation (iv) may be determined from the other four equations and there are then only four independent equations for the five nodes, that is there are $(n - 1)$ independent current equations for n nodes.

Similarly the Kirchhoff voltage equations may be written for the three loops

for loop abdc	$i_1 R_1 + i_3 R_3 + i_4 R_4 - i_5 R_5 = 0$	(i)
for loop bed	$i_2 R_2 + i_6 R_6 - i_3 R_3 = 0$	(ii)
for loop abedc	$i_1 R_1 + i_2 R_2 + i_6 R_6 + i_4 R_4 - i_5 R_5 = 0$	(iii)

and there appear to be three equations for three loops. But again, equation (iii) may be derived from equations (i) and (ii) and there are only two independent voltage equations. This means that there are only two independent loops.

It is not easy to see by inspection how many independent loops exist in a network and it is here that elementary topology theory helps. The topological graph of a network is a 'line and point' diagram depicting how the nodes of a network are interconnected by the branches. Hence the circuit shown in fig. 1.11 has the graph shown in fig. 2.2. The sequential construction of such a topological graph

Figure 2.2   Graph of circuit shown in fig. 1.11

reveals the relationship which exists between the branches, nodes and independent loops of the circuit. Consider the construction of such a graph as shown in fig. 2.3.

Beginning with the ground (or reference) node g and adding to it branch 1 a second node a is added. The addition of branch 2 adds a third node b but no loops have yet been created. If now a branch 3 is added between nodes a and b no further nodes are added but an independent loop is created, loop 312. The addition of branch 4 also adds no further nodes but creates two loops formed by the

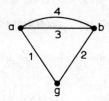

Figure 2.3   Construction of a topological graph

branches 4, 1, 2 and 4, 3. These loops, however, are not independent because loop 4, 1, 2 can be obtained by adding loop 1, 3, 2 to loop 4, 3. Hence the addition of branch 4 adds only one *independent* loop. It now becomes clear that every time a branch is added *either* a new node *or* an independent loop is created. Thus, apart from the ground node, the number of branches must equal the number of nodes plus the number of independent loops and this is the basic theory of topology, that is

$$b = (n - 1) + l \tag{2.1}$$

where b is the number of branches,
l is the number of independent loops, and
n is the number of nodes.

As an example consider the topological graph shown in fig. 2.4. There are 14 branches, 9 nodes and hence there will be 6 independent loops yielding 6 independent voltage equations.

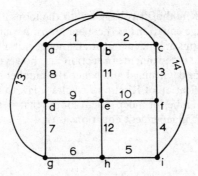

Figure 2.4   A topological graph

2.2   The basic method of network analysis

A network consisting of b branches has $2b$ unknown variables which require a total of $2b$ equations to obtain their solution. It is therefore necessary to examine the available equations to determine whether there are sufficient. It is necessary first, however, to state what the variables are, as a choice exists. The obvious choice for the variables in a problem are the branch voltages and currents but there are many other sets of variables which may be used. Consider the network of fig. 2.4. A possible choice of voltage variables are the voltages between eight of the nodes and a common ninth node, that is v_{ab}, v_{ac}, v_{ad}, v_{ae}, etc. Another choice is pairs of node voltages such as v_{ae}, v_{bf}, v_{cd}, etc. Similarly, instead of using the branch currents as variables one may choose to use loop currents, for example i_{abed}, i_{bcfe}, i_{abcgd}, i_{ebcf}, i_{hgde}, etc. There is thus a very large number of ways in which the variables may be chosen.

Assuming that the branch voltages and currents are chosen as the $2b$ variables, a set of independent equations $2b$ in number must now be determined. Consider first the branch volt–ampere equations. If the branch is, say, a resistance then the volt-ampere equation is

$$v = Ri$$

and as there are b branches there must obviously be b independent volt–ampere equations. The branch volt–ampere equations thus provide half the required number of equations (that is b).

The equations obtained from the application of Kirchhoff's current law to each node obviously yields n current equations but are they independent? Consider that a network is set up branch by branch as in section 2.1. The first branch between the ground node and the node a provides only one current equation because only one current exists and it flows through both nodes. But the addition of any other *node* provides an additional current equation and each additional current equation must be independent because it includes a parameter not included before, namely the branch necessary to set up a new node. If a branch is added between any two existing nodes it will not provide an independent current equation because it merely changes the parameters in the equations already existing from the application of Kirchhoff's current law to the nodes concerned. Thus the number of independent equations provided by the application of Kirchhoff's current law to the nodes of the network is one less than the number of nodes [that is $(n - 1)$].

The application of Kirchhoff's voltage law to the loops of the network will result in as many voltage equations as there are loops. As shown in the section 2.1, however, not all the loops are independent and hence not all the voltage equations resulting from them are independent. In section 2.1, however, the number of independent loops l was determined and hence the number of independent equations resulting from the application of Kirchhoff's voltage law to the independent loops must be equal to the number of independent loops (that is, l).

The total number of independent equations is thus

$$b + (n - 1) + l$$

but from section 2.1

$$1 = b - (n - l)$$

Thus the total number of independent equations = $2b$. As $2b$ equations exist to determine $2b$ unknowns therefore simple algebraic methods will afford a solution.

2.2.1   Worked example

Consider the circuit shown in fig. 2.5. It is required to determine all the currents and voltages.

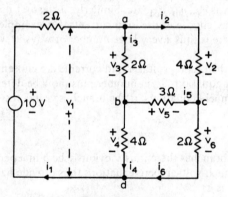

Figure 2.5

Here $n = 4$, $b = 6$, therefore $l = 3$. The branch equations are

$$v_1 = -10 + 2i_1; v_2 = 4i_2; v_3 = 2i_3$$
$$v_4 = 4i_4; v_5 = 3i_5; v_6 = 2i_6$$

Three node equations are

node a	$i_1 - i_2 - i_3 = 0$
node b	$i_3 - i_4 - i_5 = 0$
node c	$i_2 + i_5 - i_6 = 0$

Three loop equations are

$$\text{loop dab} \qquad v_1 + v_3 + v_4 = 0$$
$$\text{loop acb} \qquad v_2 - v_5 - v_3 = 0$$
$$\text{loop cdb} \qquad v_6 - v_4 + v_5 = 0$$

There are thus 12 equations and 12 unknowns and the magnitude of all the branch voltages and currents may be found.

2.3   Mesh analysis

The solution of network problems by the basic method is exact but laborious, tedious, time consuming and usually unnecessary. By the judicious choice of variables many of the $2b$ equations of the basic method may be satisfied merely by the notation. By writing the equations in a systematic and methodical way more of the $2b$ equations may be satisfied. This is of obvious importance when dealing with complicated systems because of the necessity to operate with as few variables and equations as possible. Two systems which accomplish this are the *mesh–current* and *node–voltage* methods.

2.3.1   *Mesh currents*

The powerful method of network analysis known as mesh analysis or the mesh–current method is based upon two simple but ingenious ideas. Firstly, instead of using both voltages and currents as unknown variables, it is possible to use currents only. Thus, by the use of the branch volt–ampere equations, the branch voltages are written in terms of the branch currents and the number of unknown variables is reduced from $2b$ to b. The branch volt–ampere equations are still satisfied but they are not stated explicitly. Secondly, it is possible to reduce the number of current variables required to solve the network by expressing some of the currents in terms of others. The application of Kirchhoff's current law to any node in the network will result in a relationship between the currents associated with the node and this relationship can then be used to eliminate one of the currents associated with the node. It was shown in section 2.1 that $(n - 1)$ independent equations resulted from the application of Kirchhoff's current law to the nodes of a network and hence $(n - 1)$ current variables may be eliminated by using these independent equations. Thus the number of current variables required to solve the network and hence the number of equations needed is reduced from b to $b - (n - 1)$. But from the basic law of topology, $b - (n - 1) = l$.

In comparison with the basic method the numbers of variables and independent equations is thus reduced from $2b$ to l. As an example, if this procedure is carried out for the circuit whose graph is shown in fig. 2.4, the number of unknown variables and equations required is reduced from 28 to 6.

The number of unknown current variables is thus reduced to l or the number of independent loops and a choice now exists as to which currents should be selected as the set of unknown variables bearing in mind that the number of current variables needed is now less than the total number of branch currents. The obvious choice is to select those currents which flow around the independent loops as they are obviously independent and of the right number. Loop currents also satisfy Kirchhoff's current law because they enter and leave any node in their path. The concept of using currents flowing in loops rather than through individual branches is a very important one and is discussed below in the context of mesh currents.

As there are now l unknown variables, l independent equations are necessary for a solution and the application of Kirchoff's voltage law to the independent loops obviously satisfies this requirement.

If a network is *planar* (that is it may be set out as a topological graph with no two lines intersecting) a special set of independent loops is possible, and the most obvious set is the *meshes* of the network. A mesh in a network is derived from the mesh of a fisherman's net and it therefore consists of the branches around a space in the network. Considering the circuit shown in fig. 2.4 then abed, bcfe, and fihe are all meshes, although the network itself is non-planar.

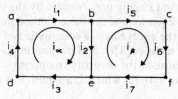

Figure 2.6   Illustration of mesh currents

Consider the topological graph shown in fig. 2.6 which has six nodes and seven branches. There are thus seven branch currents and seven branch voltages. If two mesh currents i_α and i_β are assumed to flow clockwise around the two meshes as shown, then all of the branch currents may be specified in terms of the two mesh currents. Thus

$$i_1 = i_4 = i_3 = i_\alpha$$
$$i_5 = i_6 = i_7 = i_\beta$$

and

$$i_2 = i_\alpha - i_\beta$$

The last equation is obtained from the application of Kirchhoff's current law to node b.

It is therefore seen that the current in any branch is the algebraic sum of all the mesh currents flowing in it. The mesh currents are usually assumed to flow in a clockwise direction around the meshes and thus if the network is planar then each branch current will be equal to either a single mesh current or the difference between two mesh currents.

2.3.2   Method of mesh analysis

The solution of a planar network by mesh analysis is accomplished by the following procedure. Firstly, the mesh currents, usually assumed to flow in a clockwise direction, are assigned as the unknown variables. Secondly, a set of simultaneous independent equations linking the mesh currents is formed by the application of Kirchhoff's voltage law to the meshes. Thirdly, algebraic techniques are used to solve the simultaneous equations to obtain the mesh currents. Fourthly, the branch currents are obtained from the mesh currents. Fifthly, the branch voltages are obtained from the branch currents by the use of the branch volt–ampere equations.

2.3.3   Worked example

Solve the circuit of fig. 2.5 by mesh analysis.

Assign three clockwise mesh currents as

i_α in mesh abd

i_β in mesh acb

i_γ in mesh bcd

Writing Kirchhoff's voltage law for the three meshes gives

mesh abd $-10 + 2(i_\alpha) + 2(i_\alpha - i_\beta) + 4(i_\alpha - i_\gamma) = 0$

mesh acb $4(i_\beta) + 3(i_\beta - i_\gamma) + 2(i_\beta - i_\alpha) = 0$

mesh bcd $3(i_\gamma - i_\beta) + 2(i_\gamma) + 4(i_\gamma - i_\alpha) = 0$

Simplifying gives

$$8i_\alpha - 2i_\beta - 4i_\gamma = 10$$
$$-2i_\alpha + 9i_\beta - 3i_\gamma = 0$$
$$-4i_\alpha - 3i_\beta + 9i_\gamma = 0$$

Thus three equations exist to determine the three unknown mesh currents. The branch currents may then be determined as

$$i_1 = i_\alpha, \qquad i_2 = i_\beta, \qquad i_3 = i_\alpha - i_\beta$$
$$i_4 = i_\alpha - i_\gamma, \qquad i_5 = i_\gamma - i_\beta, \qquad i_6 = i_\gamma$$

The branch voltages are then determined from the branch volt–ampere equations

$$v_1 = 2i_1 - 10, \qquad v_2 = 4i_2, \qquad v_3 = 2i_3, \text{ etc.}$$

2.3.4   General solution

Consider the problem of 2.3.3; the matrix of the coefficients of the equations is

$$\begin{bmatrix} +8 & -2 & -4 \\ -2 & +9 & -3 \\ -4 & -3 & +9 \end{bmatrix}$$

about which the following points should be noted:

(i)   All the terms on the principal diagonal are positive

(ii)   All the other terms are negative

(iii)   The matrix is symmetrical about the principal diagonal

(iv)   All the terms may be written down by inspection from the problem.

The last point is explained as follows:

(i)   the terms on the principal diagonal consist of the total resistances through which the three mesh currents flow

(ii) the other terms are resistances which are common to two meshes; for example, the 3 Ω resistance is common to meshes β and γ.

It is therefore possible to write down the matrix directly for any network without writing down the voltage law equations and simplifying them. Consider the case of a general planar network which contains n meshes. If currents are assumed to flow clockwise around each mesh and Kirchhoff's voltage law is written for each mesh then the resulting voltage equations are

$$
\begin{aligned}
R_{11}i_1 - R_{12}i_2 - \ldots - R_{1n}i_n &= v_1 \\
-R_{21}i_1 + R_{22}i_2 - \ldots - R_{2n}i_n &= v_2 \\
\vdots \qquad \vdots \qquad\quad \vdots \qquad \vdots & \\
-R_{n1}i_1 - R_{n2}i_2 - \ldots + R_{nn}i_n &= v_n
\end{aligned}
\qquad (2.2)
$$

where R_{nn} is the total resistance through which mesh current i_n flows,

R_{2n} is the resistance which is common to meshes 2 and n,

i_n is the mesh current in mesh n, and

v_n is the sum of the source voltage tending to produce *clockwise* currents in mesh n.

Matrix methods may then be used to obtain the mesh currents.

2.4   Nodal analysis

Nodal analysis is a network analysis technique based upon similar ideas to those of mesh analysis and it may be considered to be slightly more powerful in that it may be used for non-planar networks. Here, only voltages are used as unknown network variables and the branch volt–ampere equations are used to express the branch currents in terms of the branch voltages. Again, it is also possible to reduce the number of voltage variables by expressing some voltages in terms of others. This is done by writing Kirchhoff's voltage law for a loop and using the resulting equation to express one of the loop voltages in terms of the others. It is therefore possible to eliminate as many voltage variables as there are independent loops and the number of voltage variables required to solve the network is reduced from b to $b - l$. The basic law of topology states that $b - l = n - 1$ and thus the number of voltage variables required is equal to the number of independent nodes (that is, $n - 1$) and a similar number of equations is required for a solution.

Again, a choice now exists as to which voltage variables to select as the set of unknown variables bearing in mind that the number of voltage variables required is less than the number of branch voltages. As $(n - 1)$ independent voltages are needed, the obvious choice is the voltages of $(n - 1)$ of the nodes with respect to the 'nth' or ground node as these must all be independent. These node–to–ground or node–to–datum voltages are usually simply called node voltages and their relationship to the branch voltages is easily seen. Consider the circuit of fig. 2.7.

There are 9 branches and 6 nodes.

Denoting node e as the ground node and letting the voltages at nodes a, b, c, d, f, with respect to e be v_a, v_b, v_c, v_d, v_f, then the branch voltages are

$$
\begin{aligned}
v_1 &= v_a - v_b \\
v_2 &= v_b - v_c \\
v_6 &= v_b - v_d \\
v_5 &= v_b \qquad \text{etc.}
\end{aligned}
$$

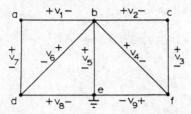

Figure 2.7 Illustration of node voltages

To prove that the node voltages obey Kirchhoff's law, write the voltage equation for any loop.

For example, for loop abd

$$v_1 + v_6 - v_7 = 0$$

Substituting node voltages for branch voltages gives

$$(v_a - v_b) + (v_b - v_d) - (v_a - v_d) = 0$$

which is so.

2.4.1 Method of nodal analysis

The solution of a network by nodal analysis is accomplished by the following procedure. Firstly, a ground or datum node is selected and the voltages of all the other nodes with respect to the ground node are chosen as the unknown variables. Secondly, a set of independent simultaneous equations linking the node voltages is formed by the application of Kirchhoff's current law to all the nodes with the exception of the ground node. Thirdly, algebraic techniques are used to solve the simultaneous equations to obtain the node voltages. Fourthly, the branch voltages are obtained from the node voltages. Fifthly, the branch currents are obtained from the branch voltages by the use of the branch volt–ampere equations.

2.4.2 Worked example

Solve the circuit of figure 2.5 by nodal analysis. Assign node d as the ground node. Writing Kirchhoff's current law at each node.

node a $\quad (v_a - 10) \times \frac{1}{2} + (v_a - v_b) \times \frac{1}{2} + (v_a - v_c) \times \frac{1}{4} = 0$

node b $\quad (v_b - v_a) \times \frac{1}{2} + (v_b - v_c) \times \frac{1}{3} + v_b \times \frac{1}{4} = 0$

node c $\quad (v_c - v_b) \times \frac{1}{3} + (v_c - v_a) \times \frac{1}{4} + v_c \times \frac{1}{2} = 0$

Thus

$$v_a(\tfrac{1}{2} + \tfrac{1}{2} + \tfrac{1}{4}) - v_b(\tfrac{1}{2}) - v_c(\tfrac{1}{4}) = \tfrac{10}{2}$$

$$-v_a(\tfrac{1}{2}) - v_b(\tfrac{1}{2} + \tfrac{1}{3} + \tfrac{1}{4}) - v_c(\tfrac{1}{3}) = 0$$

$$-v_a(\tfrac{1}{4}) - v_b(\tfrac{1}{3}) + v_c(\tfrac{1}{3} + \tfrac{1}{4} + \tfrac{1}{2}) = 0$$

and three equations exist to give the three unknowns.

The branch voltages are then

$$v_3 = v_a - v_b, \ v_2 = v_a - v_c, \ v_6 = v_c,$$

$$v_4 = v_b, \ v_1 = -v_a.$$

The branch currents are then

$$i_1 = \frac{v_1 + 10}{2}, \quad i_2 = \frac{v_2}{4}, \quad i_3 = \frac{v_3}{2},$$

$$i_4 = \frac{v_4}{4}, \quad i_5 = \frac{v_5}{3}, \quad i_6 = \frac{v_6}{2}$$

2.4.3   General solution

The matrix of the current equation coefficients of the problem solved in section 2.4.2 is

$$\begin{bmatrix} (\frac{1}{2} + \frac{1}{2} + \frac{1}{4}) & -\frac{1}{2} & -\frac{1}{4} \\ -\frac{1}{2} & (\frac{1}{2} + \frac{1}{3} + \frac{1}{4}) & -\frac{1}{3} \\ -\frac{1}{4} & -\frac{1}{3} & (\frac{1}{3} + \frac{1}{4} + \frac{1}{2}) \end{bmatrix}$$

Points similar to those of section 2.3.4 should be noted about the above matrix.

(i)   All the terms on the principal diagonal are positive.
(ii)   All the other terms are negative.
(iii)   The matrix is symmetrical about the principal diagonal.
(iv)   All the terms may be written down by inspection.

The explanation of the last point is:

(i)   The terms on the principal diagonal consist of the sum of the conductances connected to the node under consideration.
(ii)   The other terms consist of conductances connected between two particular nodes; for example the $\frac{1}{3}$ siemens conductance is connected between nodes b and c.

Again it is therefore possible to write down the matrix directly for any network without writing down the current law equations and simplifying them in order to get the matrix. In a similar way to that discussed for the general mesh analysis, consider the case of a general network which contains n independent nodes [that is, $(n + 1)$ nodes]. If the node voltages are assumed to be positive with respect to the ground node and Kirchhoff's current law is written for the n nodes then the resulting voltage equations are

$$\begin{aligned} G_{11}v_1 - G_{12}v_2 - \ldots - G_{1n}v_n &= I_1 \\ -G_{21}v_1 + G_{22}v_2 - \ldots - G_{2n}v_n &= I_2 \\ \vdots \qquad \vdots \qquad \vdots \qquad \vdots \\ -G_{n1}v_1 - G_{n2}v_2 - \ldots + G_{nn}v_n &= I_n \end{aligned} \qquad (2.3)$$

where G_{nn} is the total conductance connected to node n,
G_{2n} is the conductance connected between nodes 2 and n,
v_n is node voltage of node n, and
I_n is the sum of the source currents associated with node n and tending to produce a positive voltage at node n.

2.4.4 Mesh or nodal analysis?

When confronted by a particular circuit it is a legitimate question to ask 'Which method of solution? Mesh or nodal?' The answer is usually 'The one which results in the fewer equations.' Parallel type circuits containing few nodes and large numbers of branches are best solved by nodal analysis. Series type circuits containing large numbers of nodes and few meshes are best solved by mesh analysis.

2.5 Duality

Examination of the two methods of analysis presented in sections 2.3 and 2.4 reveals a number of similarities and analogies between the methods. The two methods contain the same sequence of ideas and result in similar solutions, but with an interchange in pairs of the variables, elements and concepts involved. This similarity is a result of the *principle of duality* which is a powerful tool in the solution of networks.

The property of duality is very general but in the context of networks, two networks are said to be dual if the mesh equations are written for one network and the nodal equations are written for the other and it is seen that the two sets of equations are identical save that the variables in one set are currents and in the other set are voltages. For this to be so, the variables and elements of one system must be the duals of the other. It is therefore possible to examine the dual quantities and concepts. From the definition of duality it is obvious that current and voltage, the principal variables, are duals and so are meshes and nodes (or loops and node pairs) which are the principal concepts. Similarly, as zero current implies an open circuit and zero voltage a short circuit, these two physical constraints must also be duals. In terms of elements, if the mutual elements between meshes are resistances then the mutual elements between nodes in the dual circuits will be conductances. A list of duals is given below.

Duals

current	voltage
branch current	branch voltage
mesh or loop	node or node pair
number of loops, l	number of node pairs, $n-1$
mesh current	node voltage
short circuit	open circuit
parallel paths	series paths
resistance	conductance
capacitance	inductance
source voltage, V	source current, I

2.5.1 Dual networks

Two networks are considered to be dual if the mesh analysis of one results in similar equations to those obtained by analysing the second by nodal analysis. It is therefore apparent that the topological graphs of the two networks will contain the same number of branches. Furthermore, the number of independent node pairs in one must be equal to the number of independent loops in the other, or put more simply, the number of independent nodes referred to a ground node in one is equal to the number of meshes in the other. This is apparent from an examination of the matrices derived for general n mesh and n independent node networks derived in section 2.3 and section 2.4. Similarly, the equations relating the branch currents to the mesh currents from one network are identical to the equations relating the branch voltages and node voltages in the other. Thus dual elements in the dual networks obey the same law and the electrical behaviour of one of two duals may be obtained from the other by interchanging voltages and currents.

The simplest pair of dual elements are resistance and conductance. Thus if a resistance in a network has a value of 5 Ω its volt–ampere equation is

$$v = 5i$$

The dual element in the dual network has a conductance of 5 S and its volt–ampere equation is

$$i = 5v$$

If the resistance of 5 Ω has a current of 3 A flowing through it then the voltage across it is 15 V. Thus the power dissipated is I^2R which is 45 W.

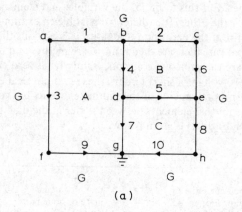

(a)

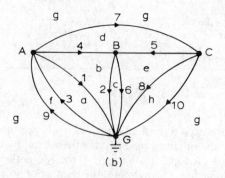

(b)

Figure 2.8   Graphs of dual circuits

The dual situation is that the conductance of 5 S has a voltage of 3 V across it and a current of 15 A through it. Thus the power dissipated is G^2V which is 45 W.

Consider the circuit shown in fig. 2.8(a). Suppose it is necessary to construct its dual. By observation the network has three meshes (A, B, and C); ten branches (1–10) and 7 independent nodes (a, b, c, d, e, f and h with reference to the ground node g).

The dual network must therefore consists of three independent nodes (A, B and C with reference to a ground node G); ten branches (1–10) and seven meshes (a, b, c, d, e, f and h with an outer space g). Setting out three nodes A, B and C and a ground node G as shown in fig. 2.8(b), the construction of the dual is as follows:

(i)   Between meshes A and B of original network is branch 4; therefore place branch 4 between node A and B of dual.
(ii) Between meshes B and C of original is branch 5; set out branch 5 between nodes B and C.
(iii) Branch 7 lies between meshes A and C; set out branch 7 between nodes A and C.
(iv) Branches 1, 3 and 9 lie between mesh A and the outer space G; set out branches 1, 3 and 9 between nodes A and G.
(v)   Branches 2 and 6 lie between mesh B and the outer space; set out branches 2 and 6 between nodes B and G.
(vi) Branches 8 and 10 lie between mesh C and the outer space; set out branches 8 and 10 between nodes C and G.

The complete dual is shown in fig. 2.8(b). It should be noted that the meshes of the original correspond to nodes on the dual and vice versa. Also, the branches have the same *numerical* values but they are now the duals of the originals.

2.5.2 Sign conventions

The definition of duality imposes a relationship between the directions of the branch currents and voltages between dual networks. When forming the dual of a network this relationship is observed by the application of a simple sign convention, which is

'When converting from a mesh to a nodal network, if the direction of a branch current is clockwise around the mesh the dual branch current is away from the node and vice versa. If the direction of the branch current is anti-clockwise with reference to the mesh the branch current is towards the node in the dual and vice versa.'

The directions of the branch currents for the networks of fig. 2.8 are thus as shown.

In order that the polarity of source elements shall also agree with the definition of duality, a further sign convention is that

'a source element which tends to drive a current clockwise around a mesh has a dual which tends to make the dual node voltage positive and vice versa.'

2.5.3   Worked example

Consider the ladder network shown in fig. 2.9(a).

The dual is determined by placing a node at the centre of each mesh as shown in fig. 2.9(b) and erecting a line around the network as shown which represents the

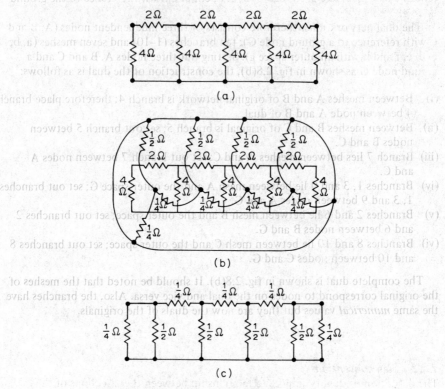

Figure 2.9   Construction of dual circuits. Resistances in ohms

ground node of the dual. The branch connecting any two nodes of the dual is formed by equating it to the branch between the corresponding two meshes of the original. The value of the dual in siemens is equal to the value of the original in ohms. Thus the dual of a 4 Ω resistance is a 4 S conductance (or a ¼ Ω resistance). The resulting dual is as shown in fig. 2.9(b) and it is shown redrawn in fig. 2.9(c).

2.6   Sources

At any instant of time a power and energy balance must exist in a network; that is, the amount of power being dissipated or stored in a network must equal the power being supplied. Until now only the circuit element which dissipates energy has been considered and the network components which supply energy to a system must now be examined.

Practical sources, which include batteries, dynamos, alternators, etc. have varied characteristics which are usually non-linear and difficult to describe mathematically.

In order, therefore, that their effects on a network may be analysed it is necessary to represent them in an idealised manner. This is best accomplished by representing the physical sources as a combination of ideal sources and ideal network elements, usually resistances.

The two forms of ideal sources have already been defined as:

(i) ideal voltage sources which are capable of supplying any current at a given voltage,
(ii) ideal current sources which are capable of supplying any voltage at a given current.

and their circuit symbols are shown in fig. 1.5.

2.6.1   Representation of physical sources

Voltage sources
Many physical voltage sources have an output characteristic similar to that shown in fig. 2.10. The output voltage of the source does not remain constant with

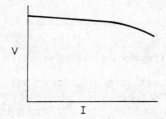

Figure 2.10   Typical physical voltage source characteristic

current but it decreases almost linearly wi.h current. Both the battery and dynamo in a car have this type of characteristic. The simplest way of representing this type of characteristic is to consider that the physical source consists of an ideal source in series with an ideal resistance as shown in fig. 2.11.

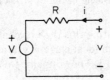

Figure 2.11   Equivalent circuit of physical voltage source

The volt–ampere equation of this representative branch will be

$$v = V + iR \tag{2.4}$$

(Note that the current flows *into* the source; this is equivalent to charging a car battery.) The voltage/current characteristic will be linear as in the initial part of the characteristic shown in fig. 2.10. It should be noted that R is a measure of the slope of the voltage/current characteristic.

A further important effect is that if the voltage source is reduced to zero (that is, $V = 0$) then equation (2.4) reduces to that of a resistance. The effect on the remainder of a network to which the source may be connected, therefore, is that:

a zero voltage-source is equivalent to a short circuit.

It is therefore possible to use the representation of fig. 2.11 as a source branch in a network.

Current sources
Most of the sources encountered in everyday life are voltage sources but some current sources do exist. Some examples are; photo–electric cells as used in light meters, metadyne generators as used in military gun controls. Other devices may be

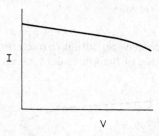

Figure 2.12   Typical physical current source characteristic

regarded as current sources, such as the collector circuits of transistors and the anode circuits of pentode thermionic valves. Many of these sources have an output characteristic similar to that shown in fig. 2.12. The output current of the source does not remain constant with current but it decreases almost linearly with current

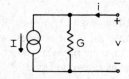

Figure 2.13   Equivalent circuit of physical current source

The simplest way of representing this type of characteristic is to consider that the physical source consists of an ideal current source in parallel with an ideal conductance as shown in fig. 2.13. The volt–ampere equation of this representative branch will be

$$i = I + vG \qquad (2.5)$$

The current/voltage will thus be linear as in the original portion of fig. 2.12 and again it should be noted that G is a measure of the slope of the current/voltage curve.

In addition, if the current source is reduced to zero (that is, $I = 0$) then equation 2.5 reduces to that of a conductance and again, the effect on the remainder of a network to which the source branch may be connected is that:

a zero current source is equivalent to an open circuit.

2.6.2 Source equivalence

Compare the equations (2.4) and (2.5) which are the volt–ampere equations for constant voltage source branches and constant current source branches respectively. If equation (2.4) is multiplied on both sides by G where $G = 1/R$, it becomes

$$vG = VG + i$$

which if VG is set to be equal to $-I$ becomes equation (2.5). Similarly equation (2.5) may be converted to equation (2.4) by multiplying by R and setting IR to be equal to $-V$.

Thus under the conditions that $R = 1/G$ and $IR = -V$ the source branches have the same volt–ampere equation and therefore as far as any external network is concerned they are equivalent and one may replace the other. The equivalence is shown graphically in fig. 2.14.

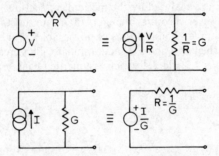

Figure 2.14   Source equivalence

Thus a voltage source branch consisting of a 10 V source in series with a resistance of 5 Ω may be replaced by a current source branch consisting of a 2 A source in parallel with a 5 Ω resistance.

2.6.3 Compound sources

If a network contains several sources in a series–parallel combination it is often possible to reduce them to a single source branch. The simplest example is two

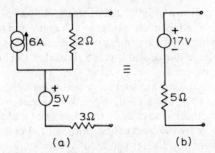

(a)   (b)

Figure 2.15   Equivalent of a compound source

ideal voltage sources in series which may be replaced by a single source of value equal to the algebraic sum of the original two. This equivalence may be proved by the application of Kirchhoff's voltage law.

But again it must be stressed that the equivalent source branch must have the same effect on the network to which it is applied as the combination of sources which it represents.

Consider a source branch consisting of both a current and a voltage source as shown in fig. 2.15(a). The 6 A current source and 2 Ω resistance may be replaced by a 12 V voltage source in series with a 2 Ω resistance. The two voltage sources may then be added to give a 17 V source and the two series resistances added to give a 5 Ω resistance. The final equivalent source branch is shown in fig. 2.15(b).

2.6.4   Resistanceless sources

Source substitutions
The volt–ampere equation for a source branch representing a physical source possesses two unknowns (v and i) and therefore when networks containing this type of source branch are analysed by the methods of sections 2.3 and 2.4 no problems arise. If, however, a source branch contains no resistance, that is it represents an 'ideal' source, then it possesses no variables. For example, if in equation (2.5) $G = 0$ then $i = I$ and v is indeterminate. This creates difficulties for the methods of sections 2.3 and 2.4 which assume that each branch has two variables.

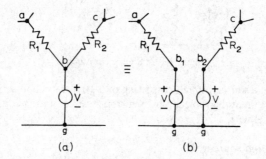

Figure 2.16   Illustration of a voltage source substitution

Consider the circuit shown in fig. 2.16(a), which shows part of a network containing apparently three independent nodes at a, b and c and a ground node g. But the voltage at the apparent node b is not variable because it is maintained at the potential V by the voltage source and it is not possible to write down Kirchhoff's current law at node b in terms of node voltages. A simple way of eliminating this problem is to substitute the voltage source by two other voltage sources of the same magnitude as shown in fig. 2.16(b). No link is necessary between the points b_1 and b_2 because they must always be at the same potential and no current can flow between them. The two sources of the equivalent circuit must therefore have exactly the same influence on the remainder of the network as the single source of the original circuit. The effect of the substitution is to replace a resistanceless source by two source branches containing resistance and also, most importantly, to eliminate a node of the original network.

A resistanceless current source may create similar problems as shown in fig. 2.17(a) where a mesh α apparently exists between nodes a, b and c. But the mesh current is not a variable as it is constrained by the current source to a level of I amperes. A simple way of dealing with this apparent mesh is to substitute the current source by two others as shown in fig. 2.17(b). The centre point of the two

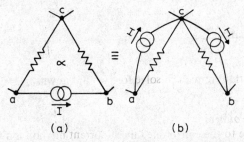

(a)   (b)

Figure 2.17   Illustration of a current source substitution

sources can be connected to node c without influencing node c because the same current is fed into and out of the node. Effects of the substitution are to replace one resistanceless current source by two source branches containing resistance and to eliminate a mesh of the original network.

Constrained mesh currents

It is not always desirable to treat resistanceless sources by source substitutions. Resistanceless current sources may be treated by the topological concept of a constrained mesh current. As was demonstrated in the discussion on source substitutions, a resistanceless current source may create an apparent or pseudo mesh in a network and therefore the definition of a true topological mesh is one which exists in a network when all the sources have been reduced to their zero equivalents; for example a resistanceless current source is replaced by an open circuit. If the source in the network of fig. 2.17(a) is reduced to an open circuit, mesh α disappears and thus mesh α is a pseudo mesh. The current which flows in a pseudo mesh is constrained by a resistanceless current source.

In mesh analysis, pseudo meshes are treated by defining mesh currents to flow in all the meshes, both topological and pseudo, but whereas Kirchhoff's voltage law equations are written for the topological meshes, constraint equations are written for the pseudo meshes.

Consider the circuit shown in fig. 2.18 which consists of two topological meshes and one pseudo mesh.

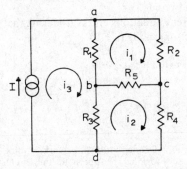

Figure 2.18   Illustration of a constrained mesh current

Mesh currents i_1, i_2 and i_3 are defined as shown.

The voltage-law equations for the topological meshes are

mesh acb $R_2 i_1 + R_5(i_1 - i_2) + R_1(i_1 - i_3) = 0$

mesh bcd $R_4 i_2 + R_3(i_2 - i_3) + R_5(i_2 - i_1) = 0$

The constraint equation is

$$i_3 = I$$

and thus two equations remain to solve for two unknowns.

Constrained node voltages

A similar technique to the constrained mesh current method is available for the treatment of resistanceless voltage sources. In the discussion on source substitutions it was shown that a resistanceless voltage source introduced an apparent or pseudo node into a network. The definition of a true topological node is therefore those nodes which remain in a network when all the sources have been reduced to their zero equivalents; for example a resistanceless voltage source is replaced by a short-circuit which eliminates the node that it creates.

In nodal analysis, node voltages are defined at all the nodes, both true and pseudo, but, whereas Kirchhoff's current law equations are written for the topological nodes, constraint equations are written for the pseudo nodes.

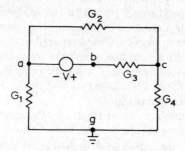

Figure 2.19   Illustration of a constrained node voltage

Consider the circuit shown in fig. 2.19. Nodes a, c and g are topological nodes whereas node b is a pseudo node.

Writing the nodal current equations and considering that nodes a and b form a supernode,[†] then for the supernode (a + b)

$$(v_b - v_c)G_3 + (v_a - v_c)G_2 + v_a G_1 = 0$$

and for node c

$$(v_c - v_b)G_3 + (v_c - v_a)G_2 + v_c G_4 = 0$$

[†] A supernode is a collection of nodes within a network forming a sub-network. A boundary may be drawn through the nodes forming the supernode and Kirchhoff's current law written for the currents crossing the boundary.

The constraint equation is

$$(v_b - v_a) = V$$

Thus three equations exist for determining three unknowns.

2.6.5   Maximum power transfer theorem

Ideal voltage and current sources are capable of delivering infinite power into a suitable load but physical sources obviously are not capable of this. In order to extract the maximum power from a physical source into a resistive load the internal resistance of the source must be taken into account.

Consider a physical voltage source feeding a resistive load as shown in fig. 2.20. What is the value of the load resistance which will absorb maximum power from the source?

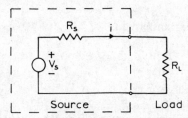

Figure 2.20   Maximum power transfer from a voltage source

The current into the load resistance is

$$i = \frac{V_S}{R_L + R_S}$$

and the power absorbed by the load resistance is

$$p_L = i^2 R_L = \frac{V_S^2 R_L}{(R_S + R_L)^2} \tag{2.6}$$

To find the maximum value of the power, set the differential of the power with respect to the load resistance to zero. Thus

$$\frac{dp_L}{dR_L} = 0 = \frac{V_S^2 (R_S + R_L)^2 - 2R_L (R_S + R_L) V_S^2}{(R_S + R_L)^4}$$

which gives

$$R_L = R_S \tag{2.7}$$

Thus the condition for maximum power transfer is that the load resistance shall be equal to the internal resistance of the source. The load is then said to be 'matched' to the source.

The value of the maximum power is seen to be

$$p_{L(max)} = \frac{V_S^2}{4R_S} \tag{2.8}$$

and it should be noted that an equal amount of power is absorbed by the source resistance.

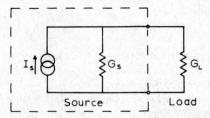

Figure 2.21   Maximum power transfer from a current source

Similarly for a current source as shown in fig. 2.21 the maximum value of power transferred to the load occurs when the load conductance is equal to the source conductance, that is

$$G_L = G_S \tag{2.9}$$

and the maximum power transferred is

$$p_{L(max)} = \frac{I_S^2}{4G_S} . \tag{2.10}$$

2.7   Network theorems

The methods of analysis discussed previously may be applied to circuits in general, but their use in large and complicated circuits, or networks, may be laborious and tedious. They do, however, lead to many network theorems which may be used to simplify a network or to provide general conclusions about its behaviour. This section states some of these theorems and shows how they may be applied to networks consisting of resistances and sources, but as will be shown subsequently, they may also be applied to networks containing capacitances and inductances.

2.7.1   Linearity

A network, system, element or source is said to be linear if at any point the effect or response is directly proportional to the cause or stimulation. A typical cause/effect characteristic for many physical elements is shown in fig. 2.22. The linear region of

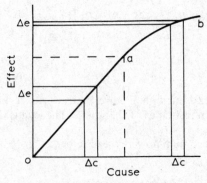

Figure 2.22   Non-linear cause-effect characteristic

the characteristic is that which lies between points o and a and it is in this region that a small increase Δc in the cause will produce a small response Δe in the effect at any point in the region. The region between a and b is non-linear because the small effect Δe caused by a change in the stimulus of Δc will depend upon the operating point in the region.

2.7.2 Superposition theorem

The principle of superposition is a direct consequence of the principle of linearity and it relates to systems subject to simultaneous excitation from multiple sources. The principle is:

'The total response of a linear system to a number of simultaneous, different stimuli is the sum of the responses to individual stimuli each acting in the absence of the others.'

Consider a general n-mesh linear resistive network in which all the current sources have been replaced by voltage sources. The mesh equations for the system are

$$R_{11}i_1 - R_{12}i_2 - \ldots - R_{1n}i_n = V_1$$
$$-R_{21}i_1 + R_{22}i_2 - \ldots - R_{2n}i_n = V_2$$
$$\vdots \qquad \vdots \qquad \qquad \vdots \qquad \vdots$$
$$-R_{n1}i_1 - R_{n2}i_2 - \ldots - R_{nn}i_n = V_n$$

(Note that $R_{ij} = R_{ji}$.)

The technique of linear algebra known as Cramer's rule may be used† to solve this set of linear algebraic equations such that any one mesh current may be stated in terms of the coefficients and sources only. For example, the solution for the current in mesh 1 is

$$i_1 = \frac{\begin{vmatrix} V_1 - R_{12} - \ldots - R_{1n} \\ V_2 + R_{22} - \ldots - R_{2n} \\ \vdots \quad \vdots \qquad \quad \vdots \\ V_n - R_{n2} - \ldots + R_{nn} \end{vmatrix}}{\Delta} \qquad (2.11)$$

where Δ is the determinant of the coefficient array, that is

$$\Delta = \begin{vmatrix} R_{11} - R_{12} - \ldots - R_{1n} \\ -R_{21} + R_{22} - \ldots - R_{2n} \\ \vdots \quad \vdots \qquad \quad \vdots \\ -R_{n1} - R_{n2} - \ldots - R_{nn} \end{vmatrix}$$

Expanding the numerator determinant of equation (2.11) gives

$$i_1 = V_1/\Delta \begin{vmatrix} +R_{22} - \ldots - R_{2n} \\ \vdots \qquad \qquad \vdots \\ -R_{2n} - \ldots + R_{nn} \end{vmatrix} - V_2/\Delta \begin{vmatrix} -R_{12} - \ldots - R_{1n} \\ \vdots \qquad \qquad \vdots \\ -R_{1n} - \ldots + R_{nn} \end{vmatrix} + V_3/\Delta \begin{vmatrix} \cdots \end{vmatrix} \cdots \quad (2.12)$$

The first term in equation (2.12) is the current which would flow in mesh 1 if the source V_1 acted *alone*. Similarly the second term is the current in mesh 1 if the source V_2 acts alone. The total current in mesh 1 with all the sources acting simultaneously is given by equation (2.12) and is seen to be the sum of the currents which flow when each source acts independently, which is the principle of superposition.

---

† M.I.T., E. E. Staff (1940), *Electric Circuits*, John Wiley & Sons, New York.

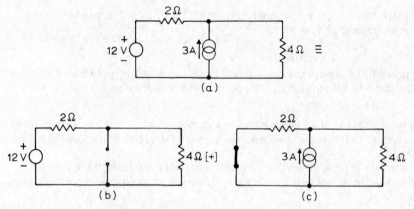

Figure 2.23   Illustration of superposition

Consider the circuit shown in fig. 2.23(a) in which the current flowing in the 4 Ω resistance is to be determined. Apply the principle of superposition and consider the sources acting individually. If the voltage source operates with the current source set to zero (that is, replaced by an open-circuit) then the circuit is as shown in fig. 2.23(b) and the current flowing in the 4 Ω resistance is 2 A. The current source is now considered to operate with the voltage source set to zero (that is, replaced by a short-circuit). The circuit is then as shown in fig. 2.23(c) and the current flowing in the 4 Ω resistance is now 1 A. The total current flowing in the 4 Ω resistance with both sources operating is thus 2 + 1 = 3 A.

The principle of superposition may also be used to characterise a linear network without a knowledge of the network components or without a full solution of the network being necessary. Consider the circuit shown in fig. 2.24. A linear resistive

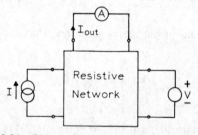

Figure 2.24   Characterisation of a linear resistive network

network is supplied by two variable sources, V and I, and the output current $I_{(out)}$ is measured by ammeter A. It is required to characterise the network by forming a relationship between the output current and the input sources. Measurements are made of the input and output variables under two conditions of operation such that when the input sources are V_1 and I_1 the output is $I_{(out)_1}$ and when the inputs are V_2 and I_2 the output is $I_{(out)_2}$. The characteristic equation of the network is formed from the principle of superposition as

$$I_{(out)} = K_v V + K_I I$$

where K_v is a constant of proportionality between the output current and the input source voltage which by dimensional analysis must have the dimensions of conductance and K_I is a constant of proportionality between the output current and the input current which must be dimensionless. It is required to determine the values of the constants of proportionality.

Putting the known values of $I_{(out)}$, V and I in the characteristic equation gives

$$I_{(out)_1} = K_v V_1 + K_I I_1$$

and

$$I_{(out)_2} = K_v V_2 + K_I I_2$$

and thus two equations exist to determine the two unknowns, K_v and K_I.

2.7.3 Star–delta transformation

Three resistances connected together at a common point O as shown in fig. 2.25(a) are said to be star- (or Y) connected. Three resistances connected nose–to–tail as in fig. 2.25(b) are said to be delta- (or Δ) or mesh-connected (they form a mesh). If the nodes (1, 2 and 3) to which the two sets of resistances are connected are part of a larger network it is possible to assign values to the two sets of resistances so that they have exactly the same effect on the network. If, therefore, the star-connected resistances are part of a network it is possible to replace them by the delta-connected ones and vice versa. The obvious advantages are that a star–delta transformation eliminates a node (node o) which reduces by one the variables and equations necessary to solve a network by nodal analysis and a delta-star transformation eliminates a mesh which reduces by one the variables and equations necessary to solve a network by mesh analysis.

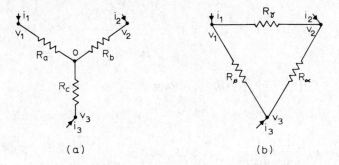

Figure 2.25   Star and delta connected resistances

Consider that in each case of the circuits of fig. 2.25(a) and (b) currents of i_1, i_2 and i_3 flow *into* the nodes as shown and that the voltages v_1, v_2 and v_3 are with reference to a ground node.

Both circuits are supernodes, thus by Kirchhoff's current law

$$i_1 + i_2 + i_3 = 0 \tag{2.13}$$

The three voltage variables are linked by the equation

$$(v_1 - v_2) + (v_2 - v_3) + (v_3 - v_1) = 0$$

The system therefore contains two independent current variables and two equations suffice to represent it.

Consider the star system of fig. 2.25(a), the voltage equations are

$$(v_1 - v_3) = i_1 R_a - i_3 R_c$$

and

$$(v_2 - v_3) = i_2 R_b - i_3 R_c$$

But

$$i_3 = -(i_1 + i_2)$$

thus

$$\left.\begin{array}{l} (v_1 - v_3) = i_1(R_a + R_c) + i_2(R_c) \\ \\ (v_2 - v_3) = i_1 R_c + i_2(R_b + R_c) \end{array}\right\} \qquad (2.14)$$

and

Consider now the delta system of fig. 2.25(b). Here the current equations for nodes 1 and 2 are

$$\frac{(v_1 - v_2)}{R_\gamma} + \frac{(v_1 - v_3)}{R_\beta} = i_1$$

and

$$\frac{(v_2 - v_1)}{R_\gamma} + \frac{(v_2 - v_3)}{R_\alpha} = i_2$$

But

$$(v_1 - v_2) = (v_1 - v_3) - (v_2 - v_3)$$

thus

$$(v_1 - v_3)\left(\frac{1}{R_\beta} + \frac{1}{R_\gamma}\right) - (v_2 - v_3)/R_\gamma = i_1 \qquad (2.15)$$

and

$$(v_2 - v_3)\left(\frac{1}{R_\alpha} + \frac{1}{R_\gamma}\right) - (v_1 - v_3)/R_\gamma = i_2 \qquad (2.16)$$

From equation (2.16)

$$(v_2 - v_3) = (v_1 - v_3)\left(\frac{R_\alpha}{R_\alpha + R_\gamma}\right) + i_2\left(\frac{R_\alpha R_\gamma}{R_\alpha + R_\gamma}\right)$$

and substituting for $(v_2 - v_3)$ in equation (2.15) gives

$$(v_1 - v_3)\frac{(R_\alpha + R_\beta + R_\gamma)}{(R_\beta(R_\alpha + R_\gamma))} = i_1 + i_2\frac{R_\alpha}{(R_\alpha + R_\gamma)}$$

Therefore

$$(v_1 - v_3) = i_1 \frac{R_\beta(R_\alpha + R_\gamma)}{R_\alpha + R_\beta + R_\gamma} + i_2 \frac{R_\alpha R_\beta}{R_\alpha + R_\beta + R_\gamma} \tag{2.17a}$$

Substituting this value for $(v_1 - v_3)$ into equation (2.16) gives

$$(v_2 - v_3)\left(\frac{1}{R_\alpha} + \frac{1}{R_\gamma}\right) = i_2\left(1 + \frac{R_\alpha R_\beta}{R_\gamma(R_\alpha + R_\beta + R_\gamma)}\right)$$

$$+ i_1 \frac{R_\beta(R_\alpha + R_\gamma)}{R_\gamma(R_\alpha + R_\beta + R_\gamma)}$$

Thus

$$(v_2 - v_3) = i_1 \frac{R_\alpha R_\beta}{R_\alpha + R_\beta + R_\gamma} + i_2 \frac{R_\alpha(R_\gamma + R_\beta)}{R_\alpha + R_\beta + R_\gamma}. \tag{2.17b}$$

In order that the two circuits shall have the same effect on the surrounding network the coefficients of equations (2.14) must be equal to those of (2.17a) and (2.17b). Thus

$$R_c = \frac{R_\alpha R_\beta}{R_\alpha + R_\beta + R_\gamma}$$

$$R_a + R_c = \frac{R_\beta(R_\alpha + R_\gamma)}{R_\alpha + R_\beta + R_\gamma}$$

and

$$R_b + R_c = \frac{R_\alpha(R_\beta + R_\gamma)}{R_\alpha + R_\beta + R_\gamma}$$

Solving for R_a, R_b and R_c gives

$$\left.\begin{aligned} R_a &= \frac{R_\beta R_\gamma}{R_\alpha + R_\beta + R_\gamma} \\[2ex] R_b &= \frac{R_\alpha R_\gamma}{R_\alpha + R_\beta + R_\gamma} \\[2ex] R_c &= \frac{R_\alpha R_\beta}{R_\alpha + R_\beta + R_\gamma} \end{aligned}\right\} \tag{2.18}$$

and

The above result may be summarised as follows. To replace a delta by an equivalent star the star resistances are

$$Y \text{ resistance} = \frac{\text{product of adjacent } \Delta \text{ resistances}}{\text{sum of } \Delta \text{ resistances}}$$

If equations (2.18) are solved for R_α, R_β and R_γ then

$$\left.\begin{array}{l} R_\alpha = \dfrac{R_a R_b + R_b R_c + R_c R_a}{R_a} \\[3mm] R_\beta = \dfrac{R_a R_b + R_b R_c + R_c R_a}{R_b} \\[3mm] \text{and} \\[1mm] R_\gamma = \dfrac{R_a R_b + R_b R_c + R_c R_a}{R_c} \end{array}\right\} \qquad (2.19)$$

which may be summarised as follows. To replace a star by an equivalent delta the delta resistances are

$$\Delta \text{ resistance} = \frac{\text{sum of the products of the } Y \text{ resistances taken in pairs}}{\text{the opposite } Y \text{ resistance}}$$

Similar results may be obtained if the elements are conductances. An important result occurs when the resistances of either the Y or Δ are equal. Substituting $R_\alpha = R_\beta = R_\gamma$ into equations (2.18) yields

$$R_a = R_b = R_c = R_\alpha/3$$

Thus the equivalent star resistances are $\frac{1}{3}$ of the delta resistances. Similarly substituting $R_a = R_b = R_c$ in equations (2.19) yields

$$R_\alpha = R_\beta = R_\gamma = 3R_a$$

Thus the equivalent delta resistances are equal and of value 3 times the star resistances.

Worked example

Consider the circuit shown in fig. 2.26(a) which is fig. 2.5 repeated. It is required to find the equivalent resistance of the circuit between points A and B.

The star network between nodes a, c and b with its centre at node b may be replaced by an equivalent delta. Substituting in equations (2.19) gives

$$R_{ac} = \frac{(2 \times 3) + (3 \times 4) + (4 \times 2)}{4} = \frac{26}{4} = 6.5 \ \Omega$$

$$R_{dc} = \frac{(2 \times 3) + (3 \times 4) + (4 \times 2)}{2} = \frac{26}{2} \ 13 \ \Omega$$

and

$$R_{ad} = \frac{(2 \times 3) + (3 \times 4) + (4 \times 2)}{3} = \frac{26}{3} = 8\tfrac{2}{3} \ \Omega$$

The equivalent circuit is then as shown in fig. 2.26(b). The parallel resistances between nodes a and c and nodes c and d may then be combined into single resistances as shown in fig. 2.26(c). The parallel combination between nodes a and d may then be combined into a single resistance as shown in fig. 2.26(d) and finally the series combination of fig. 2.26(d) is combined into a single resistance as shown in fig. 2.26(e).

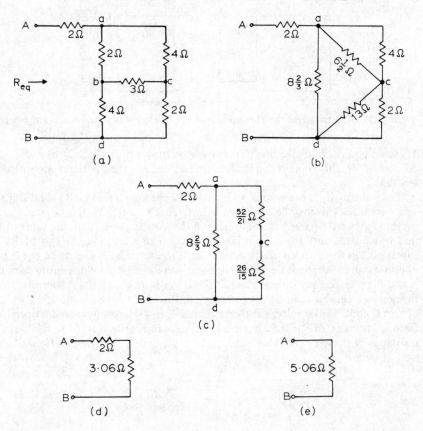

Figure 2.26 Circuit simplification by successive star–delta transformations

2.7.4 Thévenin's theorem

The treatment of the series–parallel combination of sources and resistances given in section 2.6 leads to a more general method for dealing with complicated linear networks. The method described here will reduce any linear network connected between two terminals to a single voltage source in series with a single passive branch. Networks containing linear capacitances and inductances may also be treated by this method and similar results may be obtained. The method is described by Thévenin's theorem which states:

'A linear network containing sources which is connected between two terminals may be replaced by an equivalent voltage source in series with an equivalent passive branch. The voltage source is the voltage produced at the terminals when nothing is connected to them, that is they are on open-circuit. The passive branch is the *dead* network, that is the network with all its sources reduced to zero.'

Thévenin's theorem is illustrated in fig. 2.27. Figure 2.27(a) shows a network consisting of resistances and sources connected via two terminals A and B to a load branch R_L. The network is said to be a *two-terminal* or *one-port* network. The

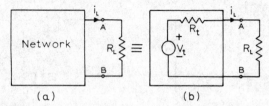

Figure 2.27   Illustration of the Thévenin equivalent of a network of resistances and sources

Thévenin equivalent of the one-port network is shown in figure 2.27(b) and it consists of V_T, the Thévenin equivalent source, and R_T, the Thévenin equivalent resistance.

The value of V_T is the voltage which would exist across terminals A and B if R_L were removed. This may be explained by reference to fig. 2.28. If a variable voltage source is inserted between the network and the load as shown then the value of V_n may be adjusted until the current flowing in the load is zero (that is, $i_L = 0$). By the superposition theorem we may then say that the source V_n is driving an equal and opposite current through the load. The total current is zero and therefore terminals A and B are effectively on open-circuit. Thus the equivalent voltage source within the network causing the original current i_L to flow must have a value of V_n which in turn is equal to the voltage at the terminals A and B when they are on open-circuit. The value of R_T, the Thévenin equivalent resistance is equal to the 'dead' resistance of the network. This may also be explained by reference to fig. 2.28

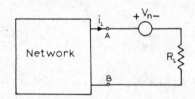

Figure 2.28   Thévenin equivalence by the addition of a voltage source

because if all the sources in the network are set to zero, that is the network is 'dead', the added source V_n will drive a current of i_L in the opposite direction around the load. Thus the 'source' which is connected to the load consists of the added source V_n plus the resistance of the 'dead' network.

A further definition of R_T is that it is equal to the 'open-circuit voltage' divided by the 'short-circuit current'. This may be explained by reference to fig. 2.27(b). If R_L is disconnected the voltage at terminals A and B is V_T. If terminals A and B are short-circuited then the short-circuit current is

$$i_{sc} = \frac{V_T}{R_T}$$

thus

$$R_T = \frac{V_T}{i_{sc}}$$

Worked example
Determine the current in the 2 Ω resistance of fig. 2.29(a). The circuit may be re-drawn as in fig. 2.29(b) and the network to the left of terminals AB replaced by the Thévenin equivalent.

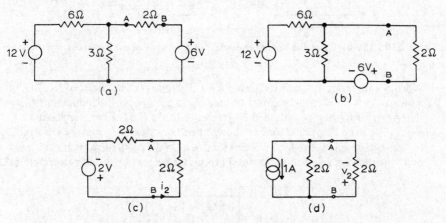

Figure 2.29   Circuit analysis by Thévenin equivalent

The open-circuit voltage of the network consists of the voltage produced across the 3 Ω resistance minus the 6 V source. The 6 Ω and 3 Ω resistances form a potential divider, thus

$$V_3 = 12 \times \tfrac{3}{9} = 4 \text{ V}$$

Therefore

$$V_T = 4 - 6 = -2 \text{ V}$$

The 'dead' resistance of the network consists of the 6 Ω and 3 Ω resistances in parallel, thus

$$R_T = \frac{6 \times 3}{6 + 3} = 2 \text{ Ω}$$

The equivalent circuit is shown in fig. 2.29(c) and the current is

$$i_2 = \tfrac{2}{4} = \tfrac{1}{2} \text{ A}$$

in the direction shown.

2.7.5   Norton's theorem
Norton's theorem is the dual of Thévenin's and it may be stated as:

'A linear network containing sources which is connected between two terminals may be replaced by an equivalent current source in parallel with an equivalent passive branch. The current source is the current flowing between the terminals when they are short-circuited. The passive branch is the 'dead' network, that is the network with all its sources reduced to zero.'

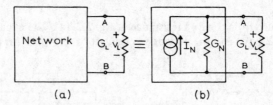

(a)   (b)

Figure 2.30   Illustration of the Norton equivalent of a network of conductances and sources

Norton's theorem is illustrated in fig. 2.30. The one-port network of fig. 2.30(a) is shown to be equivalent to a current source I_N in parallel with conductance G_N.

The value of I_N may be obtained by reference to fig. 2.31. If a variable current source I_n is placed across the load as shown then the value of I_n may be adjusted until the voltage across the load is zero (that is, $v_L = 0$). As the load voltage is zero I_n must then have a value equal to the short-circuit current of the one-port network.

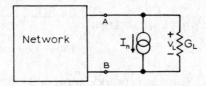

Figure 2.31   Norton equivalent by the addition of a current source

By the superposition theorem we may say that the source I_n is producing an equal and opposite voltage across the load as the network. Thus the equivalent current source within the network causing the original voltage across the load must have a value equal to the current flowing between terminals as when they are short-circuited.

The value of G_N is equal to the 'dead' conductance of the network because, with all the sources in the network set to zero, the added current source I_N will produce a voltage of v_L of the opposite polarity on the load.

A further definition of G_N is that it is equal to the 'short-circuit current' divided by the 'open-circuit voltage'. With reference to fig. 2.30(b) if the terminals A and B are open-circuited then

$$v_{oc} = \frac{I_N}{G_N}$$

thus

$$G_N = \frac{I_N}{v_{oc}}$$

Worked example
Determine the voltage across the 2 Ω resistance of fig. 2.29(a). The circuit may be redrawn as in fig. 2.29(b) and the network to the left of the terminals A and B replaced by the Norton equivalent.

By the principle of superposition the total short-circuit current consists of the short-circuit current produced by the 12 V source minus that produced by the 6 V source. Thus

$$i_{sc} = 12(\tfrac{1}{6}) - 6(\tfrac{1}{3} + \tfrac{1}{6})$$

$$= 2 - 3$$

$$= -1 \text{ A}$$

thus

$$I_N = -1 \text{ A}$$

The 'dead' conductance of the network consists of a $\tfrac{1}{6}$ S conductance in parallel with a $\tfrac{1}{3}$ S conductance. Thus

$$G_N = \tfrac{1}{6} + \tfrac{1}{3} = \tfrac{3}{6} = \tfrac{1}{2} \text{ S}$$

The Norton equivalent circuit is shown in fig. 2.29(d) and the voltage is

$$v_2 = 1 \frac{1}{\tfrac{1}{2} + \tfrac{1}{2}}$$

$$= 1 \text{ V}$$

in the direction shown.

It should be noted that the Thévenin source of fig. 2.29(c) is equivalent to the Norton source of fig. 2.29(d).

2.7.6 Reciprocity theorem

The discussion of network equivalence has until now centred upon one-port networks; the concepts involved will now be applied to two-port or two-terminal-pair networks. A two-port network requires more than one relationship between terminal currents and voltages. If a voltage is applied to one port of the network then the currents at both ports are affected. Similarly a voltage applied at the second port affects both port currents. There will thus be a total of four volt–ampere relationships describing the network and if the network is completely resistive the volt–ampere equations are simply equivalent resistances and it may be shown that two of these are identical.

The reciprocity theorem concerns the volt–ampere equations of two-port networks and states:

'In any passive linear network containing bilateral elements if a voltage V applied to a branch b_1 causes a current of I to flow in a branch b_2 then if the voltage V is applied to b_2 a current of I will flow in b_1.'

This means that an ideal voltage source and an ideal ammeter connected to different parts of a network may be interchanged without affecting their readings.

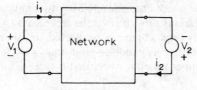

Figure 2.32   Reciprocity applied to a two-port, linear resistive network

The dual statement of the reciprocity theorem concerns the interchange of a current source and a voltmeter.

Consider the two-port resistive network shown in fig. 2.32. The mesh equations of the network will be of the form[†]

$$
\begin{aligned}
R_{11}i_1 - R_{12}i_2 - \ldots - R_{1n}i_n &= V_1 \\
-R_{21}i_1 + R_{22}i_2 - \ldots - R_{2n}i_n &= V_2 \\
-R_{31}i_1 - R_{32}i_2 - \ldots - R_{3n}i_n &= 0 \\
\vdots \qquad \vdots \qquad\qquad \vdots \qquad \vdots & \\
-R_{n1}i_1 - R_{n2}i_2 - \ldots + R_{nn}i_n &= 0
\end{aligned}
$$

if the voltage sources are in meshes 1 and 2.

Firstly, assume $V_2 = 0$, that is the second voltage source is replaced by a short-circuit (or an ideal resistanceless ammeter); the current i_2 is then (see sections 2.3.4 and 2.7.2)

$$
i_2 = -\frac{V_1}{\Delta}
\begin{vmatrix}
-R_{21} - R_{23} - \ldots - R_{2n} \\
-R_{31} + R_{33} - \ldots - R_{3n} \\
\vdots \qquad \vdots \qquad\qquad \vdots \\
-R_{n1} - R_{n3} - \ldots + R_{nn}
\end{vmatrix}
$$

where Δ is the determinant of the coefficient array.

Secondly, assume $V_1 = 0$, that is, the first voltage source is replaced by a short-circuit; the current i_1 is then

$$
i_1 = -\frac{V_2}{\Delta}
\begin{vmatrix}
-R_{12} - R_{13} - \ldots - R_{1n} \\
-R_{32} + R_{33} - \ldots - R_{3n} \\
\vdots \qquad \vdots \qquad\qquad \vdots \\
-R_{n2} - R_{n3} - \ldots + R_{nn}
\end{vmatrix}
$$

If $V_1 = V_2 = V$ for the above two conditions then $i_1 = i_2 = i$. This is so because the above two determinants are identical as $R_{ij} = R_{ji}$ and the interchange of the first row and the first column of the determinants has no effect upon the determinant. Thus a voltage V applied at either port will produce a current i in a short-circuit at the other.

The dual conditions are that a current of I applied at either port will produce a voltage of V at an open circuit at the other.

2.8   Equivalent T and Π circuits

It has been shown previously that complicated networks consisting of resistances and conductances only which are connected to other networks by a single terminal-pair or port may, by various substitutions, be replaced by a single equivalent resistance. Similar networks which are connected to other networks by two terminal pairs or ports obviously require more than a single equivalent resistance and the minimum number which may be used is three. The three equivalent

[†] M.I.T., E. E. Staff (1940), *Electric Circuits*, John Wiley & Sons, New York.

resistances of a two-port network may be connected in a T (or Y) configuration or a Π (or Δ or mesh) configuration and their values are most easily calculated by means of the pertinent two-port parameters.

2.8.1   Two-port parameters
Consider the general two-port linear resistive network shown in fig. 2.33.

The four variables which describe the behaviour of the network, V_1, I_1, V_2, I_2, are related by linear equations as shown in section 2.7.6. But the nature of the linear equations depends upon which two of the four variables are the independent

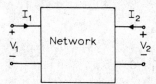

Figure 2.33   General two-port, linear, resistive network

and which two are the dependent variables, as a choice exists. As any two of four may be the independent variables there are therefore six possible ways in which the network may be characterised leading to six different sets of two-port parameters. A fuller discussion of two-port parameters is given in chapter 6 but two particular versions of two of the sets are useful in determining the T and Π equivalent circuits.

If the currents I_1 and I_2 are the independent variables of the network shown in fig. 2.33 the equations linking the voltages V_1 and V_2 to the currents are, by superposition,

$$V_1 = r_{11}I_1 + r_{12}I_2$$

and   (2.20)

$$V_2 = r_{21}I_1 + r_{22}I_2$$

and these are the characteristic equations of the network. The parameters r_{11}, r_{12}, r_{21} and r_{22} are non-physical, assigned constants of proportionality which have the dimensions of resistance. They are a particular form of the z parameters (see chapter 6).

The r parameters are defined from equations 2.20 as

$$r_{11} = \frac{V_1}{I_1} \qquad \text{with } I_2 = 0$$

$$r_{12} = \frac{V_1}{I_2} \qquad \text{with } I_1 = 0$$

$$r_{21} = \frac{V_2}{I_1} \qquad \text{with } I_2 = 0$$

and

$$r_{22} = \frac{V_2}{I_2} \qquad \text{with } I_1 = 0$$

By the reciprocity theorem (see section 2.7.6) $r_{12} = r_{21}$ and the network is said to be reciprocal. The network may thus be characterised by three parameters, r_{11}, r_{12} and r_{22}.

If the voltages V_1 and V_2 are the independent variables the characteristic equations of the network are:

$$I_1 = g_{11}V_1 + g_{12}V_2,$$

and   (2.21)

$$I_2 = g_{21}V_1 + g_{22}V_2.$$

The parameters $g_{11}, g_{12}, g_{21}, g_{22}$ are here non-physical assigned constants of proportionality which have the dimensions of conductance and which are a particular form of the y parameters (see chapter 6).

The g parameters are defined as†

$$g_{11} = \frac{I_1}{V_1} \qquad \text{with } V_2 = 0$$

$$g_{12} = \frac{I_1}{V_2} \qquad \text{with } V_1 = 0$$

$$g_{21} = \frac{I_2}{V_1} \qquad \text{with } V_2 = 0$$

$$g_{22} = \frac{I_2}{V_2} \qquad \text{with } V_1 = 0$$

By the reciprocity theorem, $g_{12} = g_{21}$ and the network may be characterised by the three parameters g_{11}, g_{12} and g_{22}.

It should be noted that the g parameters are *not* the reciprocals of the r parameters because, for instance, g_{11} is defined with port 2 *short-circuited* whilst r_{11} is defined with port 2 *open-circuited*. As the r and g parameters are constants of proportionality they may be negative.

2.8.2   Equivalent T circuits

Consider the circuit shown in fig. 2.34 which shows three resistances connected in the T (or Y) configuration.

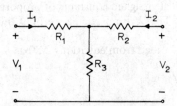

Figure 2.34   T-network of resistances

The three physical resistances R_1, R_2 and R_3 may be quoted in terms of the r parameters because with $I_2 = 0$

$$\frac{V_1}{I_1} = R_1 + R_3 = r_{11}$$

---

† The conductance or g parameters defined here should not be confused with the inverse-hybrid parameters discussed in chapter 6 which are also called g parameters. It is unfortunate that standard practice is to define both as g parameters.

and

$$\frac{V_2}{I_1} = R_3 = r_{21}$$

(because there is no voltage drop across R_2).
With $I_1 = 0$

$$\frac{V_2}{I_2} = R_2 + R_3 = r_{22}$$

and

$$\frac{V_1}{I_2} = R_3 = r_{12}$$

(because there is no voltage drop across R_1). Thus from the above four relationships

$$R_1 = r_{11} - r_{21}$$
$$R_3 = r_{12} - r_{21}$$

and

$$R_2 = r_{22} - r_{12}$$

(2.22)

The circuit of fig. 2.34, known as the T equivalent circuit may therefore be used to represent any linear resistive two-port network which may be characterised by the three parameters r_{11}, r_{12} and r_{22}. It is therefore a very useful equivalent circuit.

2.8.3 Equivalent Π circuits
Consider the circuit shown in fig. 2.35 which shows three conductances connected in the Π (or Δ or mesh) configuration.

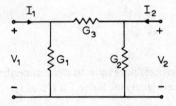

Figure 2.35 Π-network of conductances

The three physical conductances G_1, G_2 and G_3 may be quoted in terms of the g parameters because with $V_2 = 0$ (that is, port 2 short-circuited)

$$\frac{I_1}{V_1} = g_{11} = G_1 + G_3$$

and

$$\frac{I_2}{V_1} = g_{21} = -G_3$$

The minus sign in the latter relationship is due to the direction of I_2 being reversed when port 2 is short-circuited, that is

$$I_2 = -V_1 G_3$$

Similarly with port 1 short-circuited (that is, $V_1 = 0$)

$$\frac{I_2}{V_2} = g_{22} = G_2 + G_3$$

and

$$\frac{I_1}{V_2} = g_{12} = -G_3$$

From the above four relationships

$$G_1 = g_{11} + g_{21}$$
$$G_3 = -g_{12} = -g_{21}$$

and

$$G_2 = g_{22} + g_{12}$$

(2.23)

The circuit of fig. 2.35, known as the Π equivalent circuit, may therefore be used to represent any linear, resistive, two-port network which may be characterised by the three parameters g_{11}, g_{12} and g_{22}.

2.8.4   Π-T Equivalence

It was shown in section 2.7.3 that a star connected network could be replaced by an equivalent delta connected one. Obviously, the Π and T networks of sections 2.8.2 and 2.8.3 are star and delta networks and hence one may be replaced by the other by applying the theory of section 2.7.3.

Problems

2.1   Write down the equations necessary to determine the currents i_1 and i_2 in fig. 2.36 by the method of mesh analysis. Solve for i_1 and i_2.

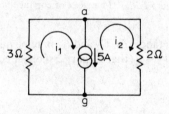

Figure 2.36

2.2   Write down the equations necessary to determine the currents i_1 and i_2 in fig. 2.36 by the method of nodal analysis. Solve for i_1 and i_2.

2.3   Write down the equations necessary to determine the node voltages v_1 and v_2 in fig. 2.37 by the method of nodal analysis. Solve for v_1 and v_2.

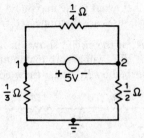

Figure 2.37

2.4   Show that the circuits illustrated in figs. 2.36 and 2.37 are duals.

2.5   Draw the circuit diagram of a network with the following mesh equations

$$15i_1 - 6i_2 - 5i_3 - 4i_4 = 0$$
$$-6i_1 + 16i_2 - i_3 - 2i_4 = 0$$
$$-5i_1 - i_2 + 17i_3 - 3i_4 = 0$$
$$-4i_1 - 2i_2 - 3i_3 + 18i_4 = 0$$

Is the network unique?

2.6   Determine the dual network of the network of problem 5 and write down its nodal equations.

2.7   Convert the circuits shown in fig. 2.38 to single voltage sources in series with single resistors.

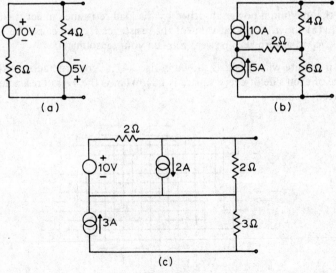

Figure 2.38

2.8   Referring to problem 1.3, what is the maximum power which can be supplied to the starter motor if the battery has an internal resistance of 10 mΩ?

2.9   Referring to problem 1.9, what is the maximum power which house number 4 can absorb if all the other houses are disconnected from the supply?

2.10   (a) If the resistance R_a of the circuit shown in fig. 2.39 has a value of 2 Ω, what value of load resistance, R_L, will absorb maximum power? What is the value of the maximum power absorbed by R_L under these conditions? (b) If the load

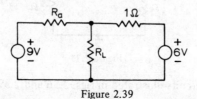

Figure 2.39

resistance, R_L, of the circuit shown in fig. 2.39 has a value of 0.5 Ω, what value of the resistance, R_a, will cause the load resistance, R_L, to absorb maximum power? What is the value of the maximum power absorbed by R_L under these conditions?

2.11   (a) What value of the load resistance R_L will absorb maximum power in the circuit shown in fig. 2.40, if the resistance R_A has a value of 6 Ω? (b) What is the

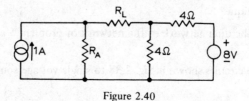

Figure 2.40

value of the maximum power absorbed by the load resistance under the conditions existing in (a) above? (c) What value of the resistance R_A will cause the load resistance R_L to absorb zero power? Explain your reasoning.

2.12   An infinite wire mesh, as shown in fig. 2.41, is constructed such that the resistance of each side of every square is 1 Ω. What is the overall resistance between two adjacent points?

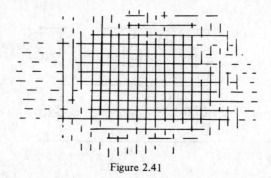

Figure 2.41

2.13   An infinite three-dimensional cubic mesh is constructed from an infinite number of the meshes shown in fig. 2.41 joined together at their intersection points by other 1 Ω resistances. Thus the resistance of each side of every cube is 1 Ω. What is the overall resistance between two adjacent points?

2.14   Reduce the two-port network of fig. 2.42 to (a) three equivalent resistances in the T form; (b) three equivalent conductances in the Π form.

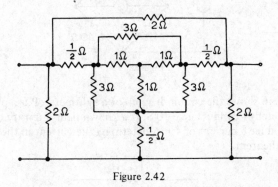

Figure 2.42

2.15   Determine the resistance between points A and B of the circuit shown in fig. 2.43.

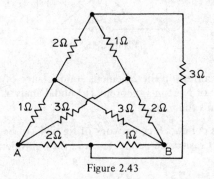

Figure 2.43

2.16   Convert the circuits shown in fig. 2.44 to single current sources in parallel with single conductances by the use of Norton's theorem.

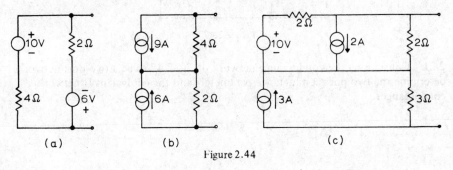

(a)   (b)   (c)

Figure 2.44

2.17   In the Wheatstone bridge circuit of fig. 2.45, G is a galvanometer of resistance 1 Ω. Determine the galvanometer current in magnitude and direction using Thévenir theorem.

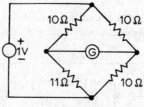

Figure 2.45

2.18   Figure 2.46 shows the circuit diagram of a lightmeter. P is a photo-cell and G is a galvanometer of conductance 10 S. If a known light intensity causes the photocell to produce a current of 1 mA determine the current in the galvanometer using Norton's theorem.

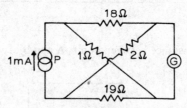

Figure 2.46

2.19   Determine the current in the 2 siemens conductance of the circuit shown in fig. 2.47 by (a) the use of Norton's theorem; (b) nodal analysis; (c) mesh analysis; (d) the use of Thévenin's theorem.

2.20   Considering the conductance network of fig. 2.47 to be a two-port network, determine the two-port resistance parameters and the equivalent T network resistances.

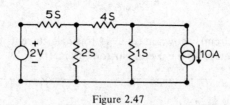

Figure 2.47

2.21   Considering the conductance network of fig. 2.47 to be a two-port network, determine the two-port conductance parameters and the equivalent Π network conductances.

3

The Circuit Elements of Capacitance and Inductance

The networks discussed previously have consisted of energy sources and energy dissipators but not energy storers. The circuit elements which store energy endow a network with non-instantaneous properties by virtue of the time necessary for them to increase or decrease their stored energy. A network consisting only of sources and resistances does not possess transient properties because the volt–ampere equations of the branches do not involve time. The volt–ampere equations of the two circuit elements which store energy contain time integrals and derivatives of voltage and current and therefore the response of a network containing these elements to a stimulus cannot be instantaneous.

The circuit theory developed previously may still be applied, however, because Kirchhoff's laws are still valid. The mesh and nodal equations may still be written but they will now be time dependent and the solution of them will involve the methods of calculus applied to integro-differential equations.

The circuit components which store energy are the inductor, which stores energy due to a current flowing through it, and the capacitor, which stores energy due to a voltage existing across it.

3.1 Capacitance

3.1.1 Definition

A capacitor is a physical device which is capable of storing energy by virtue of a voltage existing across it. The voltage sets up an electric field within the device and the energy is stored in the electric field. The simplest form of capacitor consists of two flat parallel plates of conducting material separated by a small distance as shown in fig. 3.1.

If the two plates are connected to a voltage source (for example, a battery) as shown in fig. 3.1 a continuous current cannot flow because of the gap between the plates. However, electrons will flow from the negative terminal of the battery on to plate B causing plate B to have an excess of electrons and to become negatively charged. Similarly electrons will flow from plate A into the positive terminal of the battery and the top plate will become positively charged. Thus an electric field will be set up between the plates which will remain even when the battery is removed. Energy has been supplied to the capacitor by the battery during the time that the electrons were moved through the battery potential from one plate to the other. This energy will remain in the electric field indefinitely if the capacitor is ideal, that is, if no electrons 'leak' from one plate to the other by jumping the gap.

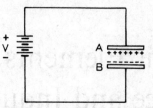

Figure 3.1   Parallel-plate capacitor

Capacitors are physical devices and they must be differentiated both from the electrical property of *capacitance* which they possess and the idealised circuit model of capacitance which is used to represent them. A definition of capacitance concerns a finite conductor remote from other bodies which is given a positive charge Q, and its potential V, which is zero at infinity, increases in magnitude. The ratio of potential to charge is defined as the capacitance of the conductor, that is

$$C = \frac{Q}{V} \tag{3.1}$$

Thus a conductor (or capacitor) which acquires a charge of one coulomb under a potential difference of 1 V possesses a capacitance of 1 *farad* (symbol F).

The dimensions of capacitance are thus

$$[C] = \frac{[Q]}{[V]} = \frac{[IT]}{[ML^2T^{-3}I^{-1}]}$$

and

$$[C] = [M^{-1}L^{-2}T^4I^2] = [-1, -2, 4, 2]$$

thus 1 farad = 1 kg^{-1} m^{-2} A^2 s^4.

3.1.2   Volt–ampere equations

The sign convention and the symbol for capacitance are shown in fig. 3.2.

Figure 3.2   Symbol for the capacitance element

The volt–ampere relationship may be derived from the definition of capacitance (equation 3.1). The voltage existing on a capacitance which possesses a charge of Q coulombs is

$$v = \frac{Q}{C}$$

But charge is the time integral of current and therefore to find the total charge on the capacitance the current must be integrated from a time of minus infinity to the instant of time under consideration, that is

$$Q = \int_{-\infty}^{t} i \, dt$$

Therefore

$$v = \frac{1}{C} \int_{-\infty}^{t} i \, dt \qquad (3.2)$$

Differentiating equation (3.2) gives

$$i = C \frac{dv}{dt} \qquad (3.3)$$

which is an alternative form of the volt–ampere equation of the capacitance.

3.1.3 Energy stored

The instantaneous power or rate of supply of energy to a capacitance is

$$p = vi = Cv \frac{dv}{dt}$$

Thus if the voltage is constant (that is, $dv/dt = 0$) the power is zero and the energy stored by the capacitance does not change. The total energy supplied to the capacitance is the integral of the power from minus infinity to the present time. Thus

$$w = \int_{-\infty}^{t} vi \, dt = \int_{-\infty}^{t} Cv \frac{dv}{dt} \, dt$$

At $t = -\infty$

$$v = 0$$

at $t = t$

$$v = v$$

Thus

$$w = \int_{0}^{v} Cv \, dv$$

and

$$w = \tfrac{1}{2}Cv^2 \text{ joules} \qquad (3.4)$$

The energy stored by a capacitance is seen to be a function of the voltage existing across it at any instant and to be independent of the current.

Consider the parallel plate capacitor of fig. 3.1. If the plates have an area of A and a charge of Q coulombs is transferred from one plate to the other then, neglecting end effects, the charge density on the plates is Q/A coulombs/metre^2. Thus, if a vacuum exists between the plates, an electric field exists in the gap of value

$$E = \frac{Q}{\epsilon_0 A} \frac{\text{volts}}{\text{metre}}$$

If the distance between the plates is d metres then the potential difference between the plates is

$$V = \frac{Qd}{\epsilon_0 A}$$

Therefore as

$$C = \frac{Q}{V}$$

where

$$C = \frac{\epsilon_0 A}{d} \text{ farads}$$

and it is clear that capacitance is a *geometric* property. The energy stored in an electric field is

$$W_E = \int \int \int \tfrac{1}{2}\epsilon_0 E^2 \, d\tau$$

where $d\tau$ is a volume element. In the parallel-plate capacitor the electric field is constant over the whole volume between the plates. Thus

$$W_E = \tfrac{1}{2}\epsilon_0 E^2 A \, d$$

but

$$C = \frac{\epsilon_0 A}{d} \qquad \text{and} \qquad V = E \, d$$

thus

$$W_E = \tfrac{1}{2}CV^2$$

which agrees with equation (3.4)

3.1.4 Capacitances in parallel
Consider the circuit shown in fig. 3.3. It is required to determine the effective capacitance of the parallel combination of three capacitances as shown. All the

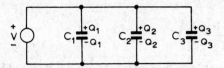

Figure 3.3   Capacitances in parallel

capacitances have the same potential of V applied from the voltage source. The charge stored by each capacitance depends upon its value of capacitance and the total charge is the sum of the individual charges. Thus

$$Q = Q_1 + Q_2 + Q_3$$

and

$$Q = VC_1 + VC_2 + VC_3$$

and

$$Q = V(C_1 + C_2 + C_3)$$

But the effective capacitance of the combination is

$$C_{eff} = \frac{Q}{V}$$

Thus

$$C_{eff} = C_1 + C_2 + C_3 \tag{3.5}$$

3.1.5   Capacitances in series

Consider the circuit shown in fig. 3.4. It is required to find the effective capacitance of the series combination of three capacitances as shown.

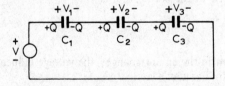

Figure 3.4   Capacitances in series

All of the capacitances have a charge of Q on their plates as shown. The potential across each capacitance depends upon its value of capacitance and the total potential across the chain is the sum of the capacitance potentials. Thus

$$V = V_1 + V_2 + V_3$$

and

$$V = \frac{Q}{C_1} + \frac{Q}{C_2} + \frac{Q}{C_3}$$

and

$$V = Q \left(\frac{1}{C_1} + \frac{1}{C_2} + \frac{1}{C_3} \right)$$

The effective capacitance of the combination is $C_{\text{eff}} = Q/V$. Thus

$$\frac{1}{C_{\text{eff}}} = \frac{1}{C_1} + \frac{1}{C_2} + \frac{1}{C_3} \tag{3.6}$$

3.2 Inductance

An inductor has been defined as a physical device which is capable of storing energy by virtue of a current flowing through it.

The electromagnetic effects of electric currents were first discovered and described by Michael Faraday in 1831. Faraday's laws of electromagnetic induction may be summarised as follows:

A voltage is induced in the following circuits:

(i)   A stationary circuit which has associated with it a changing magnetic flux,
(ii) a circuit which moves relative to a steady magnetic flux,
(iii) in part of a circuit which cuts any magnetic flux.

The direction of the induced voltages is given by Lenz's law which states that whenever a change produces an induced current, the current flows in such a direction as to produce effects which oppose the change.

3.2.1   Definition of self-inductance

A definition of self-inductance concerns a single circuit and the magnetic field linking it due to currents flowing in it. Assuming that no magnetic materials are present, a rigid circuit of given shape will create at any point a magnetic field which is directly proportional to the currents flowing in the circuit. This follows from the definition of current. The total magnetic flux Φ linking the circuit due to its own current is therefore proportional to the current I. The self-inductance of the circuit is defined as the ratio of the Φ to I, that is

$$L = \frac{\Phi}{I} \tag{3.7}$$

When the current in the circuit changes, the voltage induced in the circuit *by the current change* is, by Faraday's law

$$v = -L \frac{di}{dt} \tag{3.8}$$

The negative sign indicates that when the current *increases* the induced voltage is negative and is thus in a direction to oppose the change in the current. The most usual form of inductor is the solenoid. If the length of a helically wound solenoid is large compared to its diameter and the turns are wound close together, the magnetic flux density over the whole of the cross-section is

$$B = \mu_0 n I$$

where n is the number of turns per unit length of solenoid.

The magnetic flux across the area A is then

$$\Phi = \mu_0 n I A$$

If the solenoid is l metres long then the total flux linkage is the flux linking one turn times the number of turns, that is

$$\lambda = (\mu_0 n I A)(nl)$$
$$= \mu_0 n^2 I A l$$

From the definition of inductance

$$L = \frac{\lambda}{I}$$

Therefore

$$L = \mu_0 n^2 A l$$

or

$$L = \frac{\mu_0 N^2 A}{l} \tag{3.9}$$

where N is the total number of turns. It is seen that inductance is a geometric property.

Practical inductors are usually not 'air-cored', as the above solenoid is, but highly permeable magnetic materials are placed in and around the solenoid to increase the flux density and hence the inductance.

From equation (3.7) the dimensions of inductance are:

$$[L] = \frac{[\Phi]}{[I]} = \frac{[ML^2 T^{-2} I^{-1}]}{[I]}$$

Therefore

$$[L] = [ML^2 T^{-2} I^{-2}] = [1, 2, -2, -2]$$

The unit of inductance is the *henry* (symbol H). The henry is the self-inductance of a conductor in which a voltage of one volt is induced by a current changing at the rate of one ampere per second.

3.2.2   Volt–ampere equations

The sign convention and symbol for inductance are shown in fig. 3.5. From (equation 3.8)

$$v = L \frac{di}{dt} \tag{3.10}$$

Figure 3.5   Symbol for inductance element

(The voltage here is the applied voltage, not the induced voltage as in equation 3.8.)

A further volt–ampere equation is obtained from the integration of equation (3.10), thus

$$i = \frac{1}{L} \int_{-\infty}^{t} v \, dt \tag{3.11}$$

3.2.3 Energy stored

The instantaneous power or rate of supply of energy to the inductance is

$$p = vi = Li \frac{di}{dt}$$

and thus if the current is constant no power flows into or out of the inductance. When the current increases so does the stored energy. The total energy supplied to the inductance is the integral of the power from minus infinity to the present time. Thus

$$W = \int_{-\infty}^{t} vi \, dt = \int_{-\infty}^{t} Li \frac{di}{dt} dt$$

Since current–time functions are well behaved the variable in the integral may be changed and assuming that at $t = -\infty$, $i = 0$

$$W = \int_{0}^{i} Li \, di$$

and

$$W = \tfrac{1}{2}Li^2 \tag{3.12}$$

The energy stored by an inductance is seen to be a function of the instantaneous current only and to be independent of voltage.

3.2.4 Inductances in series

Consider the circuit of fig. 3.6. It is required to determine the effective inductance of the series combination of inductances as shown.

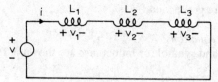

Figure 3.6   Inductances in series

The current through each inductance must be changing at the same rate since the current is common. Thus

$$v_1 = L_1 \frac{di}{dt}$$

$$v_2 = L_2 \frac{di}{dt}$$

and

$$v_3 = L_3 \frac{di}{dt}$$

But

$v = v_1 + v_2 + v_3$ from Kirchhoff's voltage law, therefore

$$v = \frac{di}{dt}(L_1 + L_2 + L_3)$$

The effective inductance of the combination L_{eff} is

$$v = L_{\text{eff}} \frac{di}{dt}$$

thus

$$L_{\text{eff}} = L_1 + L_2 + L_3 \tag{3.13}$$

3.2.5 Inductances in parallel

Consider the circuit of fig. 3.7. It is required to determine the effective inductance of the parallel combination as shown.

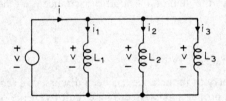

Figure 3.7   Inductances in parallel

The voltage across each inductance is the same, thus

$$v = L_1 \frac{di_1}{dt} = L_2 \frac{di_2}{dt} = L_3 \frac{di_3}{dt}$$

but $i = i_1 + i_2 + i_3$ from Kirchhoff's current law, therefore

$$\frac{di}{dt} = \frac{di_1}{dt} + \frac{di_2}{dt} + \frac{di_3}{dt}$$

and

$$\frac{di}{dt} = \frac{v}{L_1} + \frac{v}{L_2} + \frac{v}{L_3}$$

The effective inductance of the combination is given by

$$v = L_{\text{eff}} \frac{di}{dt}$$

thus

$$\frac{1}{L_{eff}} = \frac{1}{L_1} + \frac{1}{L_2} + \frac{1}{L_3} \qquad\qquad (3.14)$$

This analysis assumes that the magnetic field created by each inductance does not link with any other inductance.

3.3   Duality

The volt–ampere equations for an inductance and a capacitance are

$$v = L\frac{di}{dt} \qquad \text{or} \qquad i = \frac{1}{L}\int_{-\infty}^{t} v\,dt$$

and

$$i = C\frac{dv}{dt} \qquad \text{or} \qquad v = \frac{1}{C}\int_{-\infty}^{t} i\,dt$$

From the definition of duality it is obvious that capacitance and inductance are dual quantities. Thus the dual of a 4 farad capacitance is a 4 henry inductance.

3.4   Mutual Inductance

The electrical property of inductance has been discussed in section 3.2. It was shown that inductance is a property possessed by a circuit by virtue of its geometry which enabled it to store energy in the magnetic fields created by currents flowing in the circuit. In section 3.2, self-inductance was defined in terms of the magnetic field linking a circuit due to currents flowing in it. A similar property may be possessed by a pair of circuits which may or may not be linked electrically. A current flowing in one circuit may produce a magnetic field which links with the other circuit and if the current in the first circuit changes it will then induce a voltage in the second circuit. This is the property of *mutual inductance* first discovered by Michael Faraday. It is again a geometric property of two circuits which enables them to store energy in a magnetic field which is established between them.

3.4.1   Definition of mutual inductance

A definition of mutual inductance concerns two circuits with a current flowing in one of them as shown in fig. 3.8.

In the absence of magnetic materials, the flux Φ_2 produced by I_1 flowing in circuit 1 and linking circuit 2 is proportional to I_1. The mutual inductance of the circuits is defined as the ratio of Φ_2 to I_1, that is

$$M_{12} = \frac{\Phi_2}{I_1} \qquad\qquad (3.15)$$

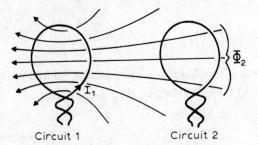

Figure 3.8   Illustration of the definition of mutual inductance

Similarly a current I_2 flowing in circuit 2 produces a flux Φ_1 linking circuit 1 and thus

$$M_{21} = \frac{\Phi_1}{I_2} \tag{3.16}$$

If the current I_1 changes, the induced voltage in circuit 2 is

$$v_2 = M_{12} \frac{\mathrm{d}i_1}{\mathrm{d}t} \tag{3.17}$$

and similarly if I_2 changes, the induced voltage in circuit 1 is

$$v_1 = M_{21} \frac{\mathrm{d}i_2}{\mathrm{d}t} \tag{3.18}$$

The signs of these induced voltages will be discussed later. As mutual inductance is a linear property, by the reciprocity theorem

$$M_{12} = M_{21} = M \tag{3.19}$$

and thus there is only one mutual inductance between two circuits.

3.4.2   Volt-ampere equations
The sign convention and symbol for two coils possessing mutual inductance is shown in fig. 3.9. Assuming that the currents are the independent variables, the

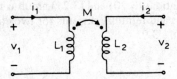

Figure 3.9   Symbol for mutual inductance

volt-ampere equations may be derived by the use of the superposition theorem. If the current in the second coil is zero, the voltages induced in both coils is then proportional to the change in i_1, that is

$$v_{1(1)} = L_1 \frac{\mathrm{d}i_1}{\mathrm{d}t}$$

and

$$v_{2(1)} = M \frac{di_1}{dt}$$

If the current in the first coil is now set to zero, the induced voltage in both coils is proportional to the change in i_2, that is

$$v_{1(2)} = M \frac{di_2}{dt}$$

and

$$v_{2(2)} = L_2 \frac{di_2}{dt}$$

If both currents are allowed to change, the superposition theorem states that the total voltage induced is the sum of the voltages produced by individual currents changing alone, that is

$$v_1 = L_1 \frac{di_1}{dt} + M \frac{di_2}{dt} \tag{3.20}$$

and

$$v_2 = M \frac{di_1}{dt} + L_2 \frac{di_2}{dt} \tag{3.21}$$

where L_1 and L_2 are the self-inductances of coils 1 and 2, respectively, and M is the mutual inductance between them.

The polarity of the voltages produced by mutual inductance may be reversed by either reversing the direction of current flow in the coils or reversing the windings themselves. The polarity reference is usually defined by placing dots on the circuit diagram as shown in fig. 3.9 and the convention is that if a current flows *into* the dot end of a coil *and* is increasing positively then the voltage induced in the other coil is positive at the dot end, with reference to the undotted end. For the circuit shown in fig. 3.9, the current enters the dot end of coil 1 and is assumed to be increasing positively; the voltage induced in coil 2 is positive at the dot end and is therefore in the same direction as the $L_2(di_2/dt)$ voltage drop.

The volt-ampere equations (3.20) and (3.21) are thus the equations linking the applied terminal voltages and terminal currents for two coils possessing mutual inductance as shown in fig. 3.9.

3.4.3 Equivalent voltage generators

The voltages induced by mutual inductance may be represented by equivalent voltage generators as shown in fig. 3.10 which is an equivalent circuit of fig. 3.9. A positively increasing current flowing into coil one at its dot produces a positive polarity of induced voltage at the dot of the second coil. The induced voltage is therefore represented by the voltage generator as shown, with the polarity as shown. Similarly the mutually induced voltage in coil one is represented by the generator shown.

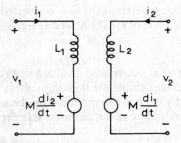

Figure 3.10   Equivalent voltage generators representation of mutual inductance

3.4.4   Coefficient of coupling

The maximum magnetic field which may link circuit 2 of fig. 3.8 and which is produced by current I_1 is the field which links with coil 1 or the self-field of circuit 1. Thus the mutual inductance of the circuits cannot be greater than the self-inductance of circuit 1, that is

$$M \leqslant L_1 \qquad\qquad (3.22)$$

Similarly

$$M \leqslant L_2 \qquad\qquad (3.23)$$

How nearly M approaches L_1 and L_2 depends upon how closely coupled the circuits are.

From equations (3.22) and (3.23)

$$M^2 \leqslant L_1 L_2 \qquad\qquad (3.24)$$

and a *coefficient of coupling* is defined which states how closely M approaches its theoretical maximum or how closely the coils are coupled. Thus

$$K = \frac{M}{\sqrt{(L_1 L_2)}} \qquad\qquad (3.25)$$

$K = 1$ if $M^2 = L_1 L_2$ and then all the magnetic field produced by one coil links with the other and vice-versa.

It should be noted that equations (3.22) and (3.23) are both necessarily true only for single-turn coupled coils; both equations do not necessarily apply to multi-turn coils. Equation (3.24) is true for all coupled coils, however, as shown in the next section.

3.4.5   Magnetic energy stored by mutual inductance

The energy stored by two circuits by virtue of their possessing mutual inductance may be determined by reference to fig. 3.9 and its equivalent circuit of fig. 3.10. Consider that coil 2 is open-circuited and the voltage source v_1 is increased until the current i_1 reaches a steady level I_1. No energy is transferred to coil 2 and the stored energy is

$$W_1 = \tfrac{1}{2} L_1 I_1^2$$

Consider that the voltage generator v_2 is now connected and increased until the current i_2 reaches a steady level of I_2. The stored energy in coil 2 is then

$$W_2 = \tfrac{1}{2} L_2 I_2^2$$

But while i_2 is increasing to its steady level a voltage of $M(di_2/dt)$ is induced in coil 1. If I_1 is maintained constant during the time this voltage is induced in coil 1, an additional voltage of $M(di_2/dt)$ must be produced by the source v_1 in order to maintain I_1 constant. This additional voltage must transfer additional energy to the circuit at the rate

$$p = I_1 M \frac{di_2}{dt}$$

The energy transferred by the additional voltage is therefore

$$W_M = \int_0^{I_2} I_1 M \, di_2$$

and

$$W_M = M I_1 I_2 \tag{3.26}$$

Thus the total energy stored is

$$W = W_1 + W_2 + W_M$$

and

$$W = \tfrac{1}{2} L_1 I_1^2 + \tfrac{1}{2} L_2 I_2^2 + M I_1 I_2 \tag{3.27}$$

The same situation holds by allowing I_2 to increase first and then I_1. The total energy must be the same in each case. This is a further proof that

$$M_{12} = M_{21}$$

Consideration of the total stored energy equation also yields the upper limit that M may have with respect to L_1 and L_2. Because the coupled circuits are passive elements the total stored energy cannot be negative therefore the right hand side of equation (3.27) must be positive irrespective of the magnitudes or signs of I_1 and I_2. If I_1 and I_2 have the same sign the total stored energy is obviously positive but consider the effects of I_1 and I_2 having different signs. The total stored energy is then

$$W = \tfrac{1}{2} L_1 I_1^2 + \tfrac{1}{2} L_2 I_2^2 - M I_1 I_2$$

Re-arranging gives

$$W = \tfrac{1}{2} [\sqrt{(L_1)} I_1 - \sqrt{(L_2)} I_2]^2 + \sqrt{(L_1 L_2)} I_1 I_2 - M I_1 I_2$$

The first term cannot be negative but it may be zero and therefore in order for the stored energy not to be negative

$$M \leqslant \sqrt{(L_1 L_2)}$$

Problems

3.1 Determine the effective capacitances of the one-port networks shown in fig. 3.11.

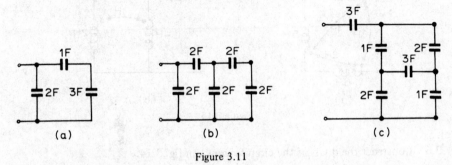

Figure 3.11

3.2 Determine the effective inductances of the one-port networks shown in fig. 3.12.

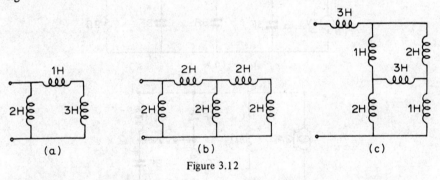

Figure 3.12

3.3 A television set is connected to an aerial via two coaxial cables in series. The parameters of the cables are

	Cable A	Cable B
Length	2 m	10 m
Diameter of inner conductor	1 mm	0.5 mm
Inner diameter of outer conductor	8 mm	5 mm
Relative permittivity of material between conductors	2.5	2.3

Determine the total capacitance of the cables. What would be the total capacitance of the cables if they were connected in parallel between the set and aerial?

3.4 Two coils have self-inductances of 4 H and 2 H and a mutual inductance of 1 H. Find all the possible values of inductance which may be obtained by connecting them in various ways.

3.5 Determine the effective inductances of the one-port networks shown in fig. 3.13.

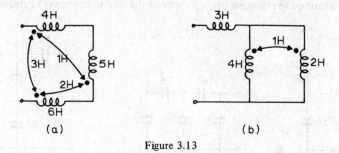

(a)   (b)

Figure 3.13

3.6 Construct the duals of the circuits shown in fig. 3.14.

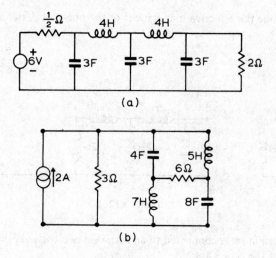

Figure 3.14

4

Transient Response of First- and Second-Order Networks

The response of networks containing only resistances and sources has been shown to be constant and time invariant. The response of networks containing capacitances and inductances is time varying because of the time necessary for the exchange of energy between capacitive and inductive elements. Expressed in terms of volt–ampere equations, the volt–ampere equations of capacitive and inductive elements are time variant whilst that of resistance is constant. Equations resulting from the application of Kirchhoff's laws to circuits containing resistance, capacitance and inductance elements must also, therefore, be time varying and they are seen to be of the particular mathematical type known as linear differential equations with constant coefficients. It is with the physical interpretation of the solutions of this type of equation that this chapter is particularly concerned.

Networks may be stimulated or excited by different types of sources; the response or behaviour of the network will obviously depend upon the source. The sources will, in general, feed energy into the network but energy stored within the network (for example, in a charged capacitance) may also provide a stimulus. If energy stored within the network is released into it, currents will begin to flow but resistance elements will dissipate the energy and eventually the currents die away to zero and, usually, no energy will remain. The network's behaviour under these conditions is termed its *natural behaviour* or *transient response*, which corresponds to the *complementary function* of a differential equation or the solution of the equation with the forcing function set to zero.

Externally applied stimuli such as a step function (for example, switching on a constant voltage source) or a sinusoidal function (for example, switching on a sine-wave signal generator) will usually result in the network's response being a final value or *steady-state response*, which corresponds to the particular integral of the differential equation describing the network plus the source providing the stimulus.

When a network is suddenly subjected to a stimulus its *total response* or complete response will be the sum of its transient response and the steady-state response. This again corresponds to the mathematical statement that the *complete solution* of the differential equation of the network consists of the complementary function plus the particular integral. The complementary function or transient response describes the transition of the network from its initial energy state to its final or constant state.

4.1   Differential equations of first-order networks

A circuit which contains one energy storage element is described by a first-order differential equation and is therefore known as a first-order network. Thus a resistance–inductance circuit is a first-order circuit. Complete solution of such an equation requires a knowledge of the boundary conditions which may easily be obtained by considering the initial and final states of the energy storage elements and how they may be represented by equivalent circuits.

4.1.1   Initial conditions

Uncharged capacitance
Consider an uncharged capacitance in a network. Immediately after the network is energised (or excited) the voltage across the capacitance is

$$v = \frac{1}{C} \int_0^{0^+} i \, dt \tag{4.1}$$

where $t = 0^+$ represents the time a very small interval after the reference or initial instant of time. The integration is carried out over almost zero time and unless the current is infinite (a practical impossibility) the voltage must be zero. An uncharged capacitance therefore behaves like a *short-circuit*.

Charged capacitance
The energy stored by a capacitance is, from equation (3.4)

$$W_c = \tfrac{1}{2} C v^2$$

where v is the instantaneous voltage on the capacitance. As shown in chapter 3 this energy is a result of a time integration of the energy stored from $-\infty$ to the time t and it therefore includes the complete past history of the capacitance. This is obviously not required when a specific time interval is under consideration and the change of stored energy rather than the total stored energy is of more importance. The total stored energy can therefore be split into two parts; that which existed before the reference time $t = 0$ and the change in stored energy between $t = 0$ and $t = t$. The energy stored at time $t = 0$ depends only upon the voltage across the capacitance at that time and the voltage depends upon the charge stored. Thus

$$v = \frac{1}{C} \int_{-\infty}^{t} i \, dt = \frac{1}{C} \int_{-\infty}^{0} i \, dt + \frac{1}{C} \int_{0}^{t} i \, dt$$

Let

$$V_0 = \frac{1}{C} \int_{-\infty}^{0} i \, dt$$

which is the voltage existing across the capacitance at $t = 0$. Therefore

$$v = V_0 + \frac{1}{C} \int_0^t i \, dt \tag{4.2}$$

A capacitance with an initial stored energy (or charge) can therefore be replaced by an equivalent circuit consisting of an uncharged capacitance in series with a voltage source. The value of the voltage source is equal to the voltage existing on the charged capacitance at the initial instant of time and the voltage source is switched into the circuit at the initial instant of time.

Inductance with no initial current flowing
Consider an inductance passing zero current and situated in a network. Immediately after the network is energised the current through the inductance is

$$i = \frac{1}{L} \int_0^{0^+} v \, dt \tag{4.3}$$

Again the integration is carried out over almost zero time and must be zero for finite values of voltage. Thus the current through the inductance must be zero and an inductance with no initial current flowing behaves like an *open-circuit*.

Inductance with initial current flowing
The energy stored by an inductance is from equation (3.12)

$$W_L = \tfrac{1}{2} L i^2$$

where i is the instantaneous current flowing through the inductance. This energy is a result of a time integration and it includes the complete past history of the inductance. As in the case of capacitance, the energy, which is dependent only upon the instantaneous value of the current, may be split into the energy existing before the reference time $t = 0$ and the change in energy thereafter. From equation (3.11)

$$i = \frac{1}{L} \int_{-\infty}^{t} v \, dt$$

and therefore

$$i = \frac{1}{L} \int_{-\infty}^{0} v \, dt + \frac{1}{L} \int_0^{t} v \, dt$$

The first integral of the above equation determines the energy stored at the reference time $t = 0$ since the energy depends only upon the current. Thus let

$$\frac{1}{L} \int_{-\infty}^{0} v \, dt = I_0$$

which is the current passing through the inductance at time $t = 0$. Thus

$$i = I_0 + \frac{1}{L} \int_0^{t} v \, dt \tag{4.4}$$

An inductance which has a current flowing through it at the initial instant of time can therefore be replaced by an equivalent circuit consisting of an unenergised inductance in parallel with a current source of value equal to the initial current flowing in the inductance. The current source is shorted out by a switch which is opened at the initial instant of time.

4.1.2   Final conditions
In networks containing resistive elements, after a long time the currents and voltages usually reach constant levels.

Capacitance
Consider the volt–ampere equation of a capacitance after infinite time

$$v = \frac{1}{C} \int_0^\infty i \, dt$$

Thus if v has a finite constant value the current through the capacitance is zero and it behaves like an *open circuit*.

Inductance
Similarly, the volt–ampere equation of an inductance after infinite time is

$$i = \frac{1}{L} \int_0^\infty v \, dt$$

and if i is finite and constant v is zero and the inductance behaves as a *short-circuit*.

Worked example
Determine the initial and final currents and voltages of the circuit of fig. 4.1(a). At $t = 0^+$, replace the capacitance by a short-circuit and the inductance by an open-circuit. The resultant circuit is shown in fig. 4.1(b). Thus

$$i_c = \frac{10}{1 + 2} = 3.33 \text{ A}$$

and

$$v_L = 10 \times \frac{2}{2 + 1} = 6.67 \text{ V}$$

At $t = \infty$, replace the capacitance by an open-circuit and the inductance by a short-circuit. The resultant circuit is shown in fig. 4.1(c). Thus

$$i_L = \frac{10}{1 + 3} = 2.5 \text{ A}$$

and

$$v_c = 10 \times \frac{3}{1 + 3} = 7.5 \text{ V}$$

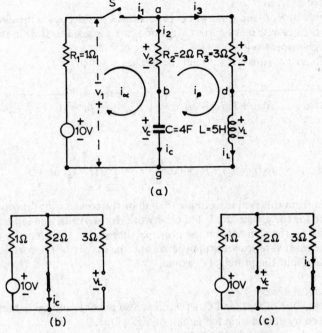

Figure 4.1   Illustration of initial and final conditions

4.1.3   Application of the basic analytical method

The circuit theory developed in chapter 2 is applicable to networks containing R, L and C elements. Each branch of the network will have two variables, a current and a voltage, and again $2b$ equations are necessary to solve for all of them. The $2b$ equations may be formulated as before but now they will be a set of simultaneous integro-differential equations rather than the algebraic equations obtained for the resistive network case.

Consider the circuit of fig. 4.1(a). The volt–ampere equations of the branches are

$$v_1 = R_1 i_1 - 10, \qquad v_2 = R_2 i_2, \qquad v_3 = R_3 i_3$$

$$v_L = L \frac{\mathrm{d} i_L}{\mathrm{d} t}, \qquad v_C = \frac{1}{C} \int_{-\infty}^{t} i_C \, \mathrm{d} t$$

The independent current law equations are

node a	$i_1 - i_2 - i_3 = 0$
node b	$i_2 - i_C = 0$
node d	$i_3 - i_L = 0$

The independent voltage law equations are

loop abg	$v_1 + v_2 + v_C = 0$
loop adgb	$v_3 + v_L - v_C - v_2 = 0$

Thus ten equations exist to solve for the ten unknowns.

4.1.4 Mesh analysis

Mesh analysis of R, L and C networks is possible. Consider again the circuit of fig. 4.1(a). Two clockwise mesh currents, i_α and i_β are assumed to flow in the meshes abg and adgb respectively.

The voltage law equations around the meshes are then

$$\text{mesh } \alpha \qquad R_1 i_\alpha + R_2(i_\alpha - i_\beta) + \frac{1}{C} \int_{-\infty}^{t} (i_\alpha - i_\beta)\, dt = 10$$

$$\text{mesh } \beta \qquad R_2(i_\beta - i_\alpha) + R_3 i_\beta + L \frac{di_\beta}{dt} + \frac{1}{C} \int_{-\infty}^{t} (i_\beta - i_\alpha)\, dt = 0$$

It is seen from this simple example that all of the conclusions drawn in section 2.3 are still true for the general R, L and C network. In particular the self-terms are still positive (that is, the elements on the principal diagonal of the general n-mesh matrix), the mutual terms are still negative and the matrix of the coefficients is symmetrical about the principal diagonal.

4.1.5 Nodal analysis

The nodal analysis of R, L and C networks is also possible and again it can be demonstrated by considering the circuit of fig. 4.1(a).

Node g is the reference node and v_a, v_b and v_d are the voltages of nodes a, b and d respectively with reference to node g.

The Kirchhoff current law equation at each node is then

$$\text{node a} \qquad \frac{(v_a - 10)}{R_1} + \frac{(v_a - v_b)}{R_2} + \frac{(v_a - v_d)}{R_3} = 0$$

$$\text{node b} \qquad \frac{(v_b - v_a)}{R_2} + C \frac{dv_b}{dt} = 0$$

$$\text{node d} \qquad \frac{(v_d - v_a)}{R_3} + \frac{1}{L} \int_{-\infty}^{t} v_d\, dt = 0$$

Thus

$$v_a\left(\frac{1}{R_1} + \frac{1}{R_2} + \frac{1}{R_3}\right) - v_b\left(\frac{1}{R_2}\right) - v_d\left(\frac{1}{R_3}\right) = \frac{10}{R_1}$$

$$- v_a\left(\frac{1}{R_2}\right) + v_b\left(\frac{1}{R_2}\right) + C\frac{dv_b}{dt} + 0 = 0$$

and

$$- v_a\left(\frac{1}{R_3}\right) + 0 + v_d\left(\frac{1}{R_3}\right) + \frac{1}{L} \int_{-\infty}^{t} v_d\, dt = 0$$

Again, conclusions regarding the matrix of coefficients of an n-mesh R, L and C network may be drawn from this simple example. The self-terms are positive, the mutual terms are negative and the matrix is symmetrical about the principal diagonal.

Thus the coefficient matrix of an n-mesh R, L and C network may be written down by inspection without the equations being derived.

4.1.6 Application of network theorems

Inductance and capacitance are linear elements and therefore it is to be expected that the principle of superposition also applies to them. With each element a stimulus will produce a time-varying response but if the stimulus is doubled then the response has exactly the same shape as the original but at any instant of time it is double the amplitude.

Superposition may still be applied because if each element is subject to two stimuli applied independently then the response of the element to the two stimuli applied simultaneously is the sum of the responses to the individual stimuli.

Thévenin's and Norton's theorems also apply equally well to R, L and C networks. In the Thévenin case a network containing R, L and C elements and sources may be replaced by a voltage source equal to the open circuit voltage of the network in series with the 'dead' network with all the sources removed.

4.2 Natural response of first-order networks

4.2.1 RC circuit

The behaviour of a circuit with one energy storage element is described by a first-order differential equation. Such a circuit is the RC circuit of fig. 4.2. Consider that the capacitance is charged to a voltage V_0 before the switch is closed.

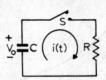

Figure 4.2 *RC* circuit with initial stored charge

The differential equation of the circuit is

$$Ri + \frac{1}{C} \int_{-\infty}^{t} i \, \mathrm{d}t = 0 \tag{4.5}$$

or, by differentiating equation (4.5)

$$R\frac{\mathrm{d}i}{\mathrm{d}t} + \frac{i}{C} = 0 \tag{4.6}$$

Separating the variables gives

$$\frac{\mathrm{d}i}{i} = -\frac{\mathrm{d}t}{CR}$$

Integrating between the limits $t = 0$ and $t = t$ of the right-hand side of this equation means integration between the initial current i_0 and i of the left-hand side. Thus

$$\int_{i_0}^{i} \frac{di}{i} = -\int_{0}^{t} \frac{dt}{CR}$$

and

$$\log_e (i) - \log_e (i_0) = -t/CR$$

and

$$i = i_0 \, e^{-t/CR} \tag{4.7}$$

But

$$i_0 = \frac{V_0}{R}$$

(from section 4.1.1). Thus

$$i = \frac{V_0}{R} \, e^{-t/CR}$$

and the current decays exponentially from a value V_0/R as shown in fig. 4.3. The product RC, which has the dimensions of time, is termed the *time constant* (T) of the circuit.

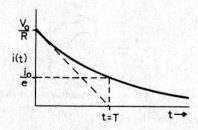

Figure 4.3   Current–time response of the circuit of fig. 4.2

At $t = T$

$$i = \frac{V_0}{R} \, e^{-1} = \frac{V_0}{R \, e} = 0.368 \, \frac{V_0}{R}$$

as shown. Also

$$\frac{di}{dt} = -\left(\frac{V_0}{R}\right) \frac{1}{CR} \, e^{-t/CR}$$

At $t = 0$

$$\left(\frac{di}{dt}\right)_{t=0} = -\left(\frac{V_0}{R}\right)\frac{1}{CR}$$

If the exponential curve continued to fall at this rate it would intercept the time axis at the time $t = T$ as shown. This is a particular case of the general property of exponential decays that if the function were to continue to decay at the rate at which it does at any instant of time then it would reach zero at a time of T seconds later.

Here, at some time $t = t_1$

$$(i)_{t=t_1} = \left(\frac{V_0}{R}\right)e^{-t_1/CR}$$

and

$$\left(\frac{di}{dt}\right)_{t=t_1} = -\left(\frac{V_0}{R}\right)\left(\frac{1}{CR}\right)e^{-t_1/CR}$$

If the current continued to decay at this rate then at a time $t = t_1 + T$ the current would be

$$(i)_{t=t_1 + T} = (i)_{t=t_1} + \left(\frac{di}{dt}\right)_{t=t_1} \times T$$

Therefore

$$(i)_{t=t_1 + T} = \left(\frac{V_0}{R}\right)e^{-t_1/CR} - \left(\frac{V_0}{R}\right)\left(\frac{1}{CR}\right)e^{-t_1/CR} \times (CR)$$

and

$$(i)_{t=t_1 + T} = 0$$

4.2.2 RL circuit

The other simple example of a first-order electrical circuit is the *RL* circuit shown in fig. 4.4. The inductance is considered to possess energy represented by the current i_0 at time $t = 0$.

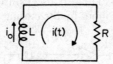

Figure 4.4   *RL* circuit with initial current flowing

The differential equation of the circuit is

$$L\frac{di}{dt} + iR = 0 \tag{4.8}$$

which is similar to equation (4.6).

The solution is, therefore,

$$i = i_0 \, e^{-tR/L} \tag{4.9}$$

The time constant is

$$T = \frac{L}{R}$$

and the natural response of an RL circuit is the exponential decay shown in fig. 4.5.

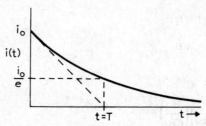

Figure 4.5   Current–time response of the circuit of fig. 4.4

The voltage existing on the resistance is

$$V_R = Ri_0 \, e^{-t/T}$$

Thus all the variables in both the RC and RL circuits have the form

$$f(t) = A \, e^{-t/T} \tag{4.10}$$

where A = initial value of function and T = time constant.

Thus equation (4.10) describes the natural or transient behaviour of both RC and RL circuits.

The complementary functions of the differential equations of the two networks are seen to describe their behaviour under a stimulus of energy stored within the circuits themselves with no external stimulation.

4.3   Some steady-state responses of first-order networks

4.3.1   Series RL circuit excited by a step function

If a first-order circuit is subjected to a step function the response is the sum of its natural response and the steady-state response. Consider the circuit of fig. 4.6. The RL circuit is subjected to a step input by the closing of the switch.

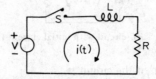

Figure 4.6 RL circuit excited by a step input of voltage

The steady-state response of the circuit is the circuit response at $t = \infty$ when the current will have reached a constant level.

The differential equation is

$$L\frac{di}{dt} + Ri = V \tag{4.11}$$

and

$$(i)_{t=\infty} = \frac{V}{R}$$

which corresponds to the particular integral.

4.3.2 Series RC circuit excited by a step function
Consider the circuit of fig. 4.7

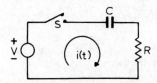

Figure 4.7   RC circuit excited by a step input of voltage

The differential equation is

$$iR + \frac{1}{C} \int_{-\infty}^{t} i \, dt = V \tag{4.12}$$

or

$$R\frac{di}{dt} + \frac{i}{C} = 0$$

This is exactly the same equation as equation (4.6) and therefore the solution is the same. The steady-state response of this circuit is that the current is zero. (The capacitance acts as an open circuit at $t = \infty$.) This corresponds to the particular integral of the differential equation being zero.

4.3.3 Series RL circuit excited by a sinusoidal function
Consider the circuit of fig. 4.8. The external stimulus is here a sinusoidal voltage wave.

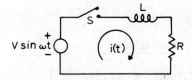

Figure 4.8   RL circuit with sinusoidal voltage excitation

The differential equation is

$$L \frac{di}{dt} + Ri = V \sin \omega t \qquad (4.13)$$

The complementary function of this equation has been determined and is

$$i = A\, e^{-t/T} \qquad (4.14)$$

where A is a constant depending upon the initial conditions.

The particular integral of the equation corresponds to the current flowing in the circuit after the switch has been closed for some time. As the excitation is sinusoidal, it is a reasonable assumption that the steady state-current will also be a sinusoidal quantity of the same frequency.

A general expression for such a quantity is

$$i_{ss} = B \sin (\omega t + \phi) \qquad (4.15)$$

and

$$\frac{di_{ss}}{dt} = \omega B \cos (\omega t + \phi) \qquad (4.16)$$

where B is the unknown current amplitude and ϕ is the unknown phase difference between the voltage and current sinusoids.

The steady-state solution must satisfy the differential equation and substituting equations (4.15) and (4.16) in equation (4.13) gives

$$\omega LB \cos (\omega t + \phi) + RB \sin (\omega t + \phi) = V \sin \omega t$$

Rearranging

$$\sin \omega t(- \omega LB \sin \phi + RB \cos \phi - V) + \cos \omega t(\omega LB \cos \phi + RB \sin \phi) = 0$$

For this equation to be true at all intervals of time the terms in each of the brackets must sum to zero. Hence

$$- \omega LB \sin \phi + RB \cos \phi - V = 0$$

and

$$\omega LB \cos \phi + RB \sin \phi = 0$$

Solving for B and ϕ gives

$$\tan \phi = - \frac{\omega L}{R}$$

and

$$B = \frac{V}{\sqrt{(R^2 + \omega^2 L^2)}}$$

The expression for the current is then

$$i_{ss} = \frac{V}{\sqrt{(R^2 + \omega^2 L^2)}} \sin \left(\omega t + \tan^{-1} - \frac{\omega L}{R} \right) \qquad (4.17)$$

4.4 Total response of first-order networks

The transient behaviour of electric circuits which contain a single energy storer has been shown in section 4.2 to be characterised by a single decaying exponential. The natural response of this type of circuit has been examined and shown to correspond to the complementary function of the differential equation describing the circuit. Similarly, the steady-state response of the circuit to a known external stimulus has been shown to correspond to the particular integral of the differential equation. This section deals with the total response of single-energy-source circuits to several of the most commonly encountered stimuli.

4.4.1 Step response of RL circuits

Consider the circuit of fig. 4.9. A step input of voltage is accomplished by closing the switch at time $t = 0$.

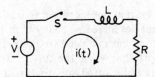

Figure 4.9   *RL* circuit excited by a step input of voltage

After the time $t = 0$, the differential equation is

$$L \frac{di}{dt} + Ri = V \tag{4.19}$$

Separating the variables gives

$$\frac{di}{\left(\dfrac{V}{R} - i\right)} = \frac{R}{L} \, dt \tag{4.20}$$

At $t = 0, i = 0$ (the inductance behaves as an open circuit); and at $t = t, i = i$. Thus

$$\int_0^i \frac{di}{\left(\dfrac{V}{R} - i\right)} = \int_0^t \frac{R}{L} \, dt$$

Therefore,

$$\log_e \left(\frac{\left(\dfrac{V}{R} - i\right)}{\dfrac{V}{R}} \right) = -\frac{R}{L} t \tag{4.21}$$

and

$$i = \frac{V}{R}(1 - e^{-Rt/L})$$

Thus the current in the circuit increases from the initial condition of $i = 0$ to the final value by means of the characteristic exponential equation of the RL circuit to the final steady-state value of V/R amperes as shown in fig. 4.10.

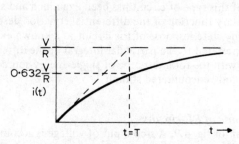

Figure 4.10   Current–time response of the circuit of fig. 4.9

At time $t = T = L/R$ the current has increased to 0.632 of its final value as shown.
At time $t = 5T$ the current has increased to 0.993 of its final value of V/R.
At time $t = 0.1T$ the current has increased to 0.095 of its final value. It is interesting to compare this value with that which the current would have reached if it had continued increasing linearly at its initial rate, that is, at $t = 0$

$$\left(\frac{di}{dt}\right)_{t=0} = \frac{V}{R} \times \frac{R}{L} = \frac{V}{R} \times \frac{1}{T}$$

Thus if

$$i = \frac{V}{R} \times \frac{1}{T} \times t$$

at

$$t = 0.1T, \qquad i = \frac{V}{R} \times 0.1$$

Thus the current in the circuit is 95 per cent of the ramp function which increases at the initial rate of the current in the circuit.
The voltage on the resistance is

$$v_R = iR$$

thus

$$v_R = V(1 - e^{-Rt/L}) \tag{4.22}$$

The dual of the above circuit is a parallel GC circuit subjected to a step input of current. It is therefore possible to infer that the voltage across the circuit would be

$$v = \frac{I}{G}(1 - e^{-tG/C}) \tag{4.23}$$

The voltage–time curve of the circuit would therefore have the same shape as fig. 4.10.

4.4.2 Repetitive-step response of RL circuit

Consider the circuit of fig. 4.9 operating as before after the switch has closed until the time $t = 5T$. The potential of the source V then reverses as shown in fig. 4.11(a). The potential of the source then reverses every $5T$ seconds as shown in fig. 4.11(a). The response of the circuit between $t = 0$ and $t = 5T$ is the same as before.

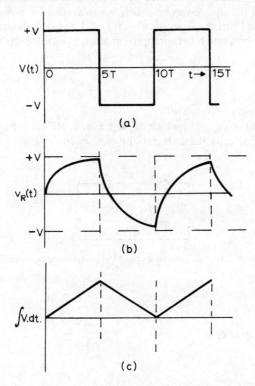

Figure 4.11   Repetitive-step response of the circuit of fig. 4.9

Consider the period between $t = 5T$ and $t = 10T$. The differential equation is now

$$L \frac{di}{dt} + Ri = -V$$

Considering the new reference for time is at $t = 5T$ then at $t' = 0$ (that is, $t = 5T$) $i \doteq V/R$, and the integral equation is

$$\int_{V/R}^{i} \left(\frac{di}{-\frac{V}{R} - i} \right) = \int_{0}^{t'} \frac{R}{L} dt'$$

and

$$i = -\frac{V}{R}(1 - 2e^{-Rt'/L})$$

The current will therefore approach the value $-V/R$ exponentially and v_R will approach the value $-V$ as shown in fig. 4.11(b).

This process continues every time the potential reverses and the quasi-triangular wave of fig. 4.11(b) is the response of the circuit to the square-wave input.

The integral of a square-wave is a triangular wave as shown in fig. 4.11(c) and the series RL circuit is therefore seen to be operating as an approximate integrator.

If the period of the square-wave is much less than the time constant of the circuit it is obvious from the analysis of section 4.4.1 that the voltage appearing on the resistance will be a much better approximation to a triangular wave than that of fig. 4.11(b).

4.4.3   Step response of RC circuit

Consider the circuit of fig. 4.12 which depicts a series RC circuit excited by a step input of voltage. The capacitance is initially uncharged.

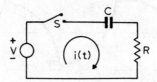

Figure 4.12   *RC circuit excited by a step input of voltage*

The differential equation is

$$iR + \frac{1}{C} \int_{-\infty}^{t} i \, dt = V$$

or

$$R \frac{di}{dt} + \frac{i}{C} = 0$$

which is identical to equation (4.6).

Therefore

$$i = \frac{V}{R} e^{-t/RC} \tag{4.24}$$

and the current–time curve is the decaying exponential shown in fig. 4.13. The voltage across the resistance is,

$$v_R = iR = V e^{-t/RC} \tag{4.25}$$

and the resistance–voltage/time curve will be a decaying exponential similar to that shown in fig. 4.13.

At time $t = T = RC$ the current has decreased to 0.368 of its initial value, as shown.

At time $t = 5T$ the current has decreased to 0.005 of its initial value of V/R.

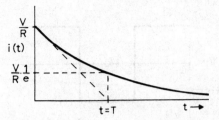

Figure 4.13   Current–time response of the circuit of fig. 4.12

The dual of the above circuit is a parallel GL circuit subjected to a step input of current. It is therefore possible to infer that the voltage across the parallel circuit would be

$$v = \frac{I}{G} e^{-t/LG}$$

The voltage–time curve would therefore have the same shape as that of fig. 4.13.

4.4.4   Repetitive step response of RC circuit

Consider the circuit of fig. 4.12 operating as before after the switch has closed until the time $t = 5T$. The potential of the source V then reverses and continues to do so at intervals of time of $5T$ seconds as shown in fig. 4.14(a). Thus the circuit is excited by a square-wave of voltage of period $10T$ seconds.

The response of the circuit between $t = 0$ and $t = 5T$ is the same as before.

Consider the period between $t = 5T$ and $t = 10T$. The differential equation is now

$$iR + \frac{i}{C} \int_{-\infty}^{t} i \, dt = -V$$

or

$$R \frac{di}{dt} + \frac{i}{C} = 0$$

But the initial value of the current will be different from the original case because the capacitance has an initial charge. It was shown in section 4.1.1 that the initial charge may be represented by a voltage source of value V_0 in series with the capacitance. Here $V_0 \triangleq -V$ and the total voltage acting around the circuit at time $t = 5$ is $-V - V = -2V$. Thus the initial current has an amplitude of $-2V/R$ amperes and

$$i = -\frac{2V}{R} e^{-t/CR}$$

The current–time and resistance–voltage–time curves will thus be the 'spiky' waveform of fig. 4.14(b).

Approximate differentiator and integrator

The differential of a square-wave is a series of infinite impulse functions as shown in fig. 4.14(c) and the series RC circuit is seen to be operating as an approximate

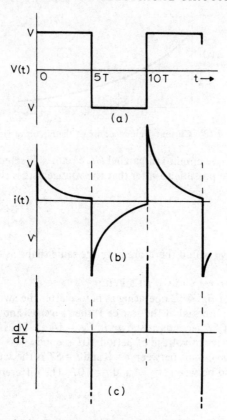

Figure 4.14   Repetitive-step response of the circuit of fig. 4.12

differentiator. If the period of the square-wave is much greater than the time constant of the circuit it is obvious that the voltage appearing at the resistance is a much better approximation to a series of impulses.

The voltage across the capacitance is given by

$$v_C = V - v_R$$

and thus for a single step is

$$v_C = V - V e^{-t/RC}$$

and

$$v_C = V(1 - e^{-t/RC})$$

which is similar to equation (4.22) which describes the voltage on the resistance of the series RL circuit.

Thus the series RC circuit may also be used as an approximate integrator but with the voltage existing on the *capacitance* being regarded as the integral of the source voltage. It should be noted also that the same proviso exists for the use of a series RC circuit as an integrator as exists for the use of a series RL circuit. Namely that the time constant of the circuit is much larger than the period of the waveform. This should be compared with the proviso for its use as a differentiator which is quite the reverse.

4.5 Differential equations of second-order networks

It has been shown previously that the behaviour of a network containing a single energy storage element is described by a first-order differential equation. The solution is a single decaying exponential function containing a single arbitrary constant which is determined from a knowledge of the initial conditions existing in the network. This section deals with networks containing two energy storage elements, namely a capacitance and an inductance. The differential equation describing the network will be seen to be a second-order linear differential equation with constant coefficients and the solution contains two arbitrary constants which are determined from a knowledge of the initial conditions existing in the network.

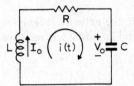

Figure 4.15   Series RLC circuit with initial stored energy

Consider the circuit of fig. 4.15. The application of Kirchhoff's voltage law to the mesh gives

$$L \frac{\mathrm{d}i}{\mathrm{d}t} + Ri + \frac{1}{C} \int_{-\infty}^{t} i \, \mathrm{d}t = 0 \tag{4.26}$$

or

$$L \frac{\mathrm{d}^2 i}{\mathrm{d}t^2} + R \frac{\mathrm{d}i}{\mathrm{d}t} + \frac{i}{C} = 0 \tag{4.27}$$

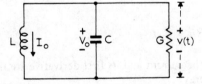

Figure 4.16   Parallel GLC circuit with initial stored energy

Consider now the circuit of fig. 4.16. The application of Kirchhoff's current law to the circuit gives

$$C \frac{\mathrm{d}v}{\mathrm{d}t} + Gv + \frac{1}{L} \int_{-\infty}^{t} v \, \mathrm{d}t = 0 \tag{4.28}$$

or

$$C\frac{d^2v}{dt^2} + Gv + \frac{v}{L} = 0 \qquad (4.29)$$

It is seen that the two above circuits are duals and the equations describing them are similar. Thus a solution of only one of them is necessary. Similarly a voltage source applied to circuit of fig. 4.15 will produce a similar response to that produced by a current source applied to the circuit of fig. 4.16.

4.6   Natural response of second-order networks

Consider the series circuit of fig. 4.15. The natural response of the circuit is the response to energy stored within the circuit. The response is described by the solution of equation (4.26) or equation (4.27). Again, the natural response corresponds to the complementary function of the differential equation describing the network.

The initial energy stored in the network is represented by an initial current flowing through the inductance and an initial voltage existing on the capacitance, that is

$$(i)_{t=0} = I_0 = \frac{1}{L} \int_{-\infty}^{0} v_L \, dt$$

and

$$(v_C)_{t=0} = V_0 = \frac{1}{C} \int_{-\infty}^{0} i \, dt$$

At the initial instant of time $t = 0$, equation (4.26) is

$$L\left(\frac{di}{dt}\right)_{t=0} + R(i)_{t=0} + \frac{1}{C} \int_{-\infty}^{0} i \, dt = 0$$

Thus

$$\left(\frac{di}{dt}\right)_{t=0} = -\frac{1}{L}(RI_0 + V_0)$$

The initial value of the current and its first derivative are therefore known in terms of the initial stored energy.

It is logical to assume that a solution of equation (4.26), as was the case for the first-order differential equation, is an exponential of the form

$$i(t) = A\,e^{st} \qquad (4.30)$$

where A and s are to be determined. Thus

$$\frac{di}{dt} = si(t) \qquad (4.31)$$

and

$$\int i \, dt = \frac{i(t)}{s} \tag{4.32}$$

Substituting equations (4.30), (4.31) and (4.32) in equation (4.26) gives

$$\left(Ls + R + \frac{1}{Cs} \right) i(t) = 0$$

For a non-trivial solution it is obvious that

$$Ls + R + \frac{1}{Cs} = 0$$

which is satisfied by two values of s denoted by s_1 and s_2 such that

$$s_{12} = -\frac{R}{2L} \pm \sqrt{\left\{ \left(\frac{R}{2L} \right)^2 - \frac{1}{LC} \right\}} \tag{4.33}$$

Since each value of s determines an independent solution of the form given in equation (4.30) it is clear that their sum is a more general solution. Thus

$$i(t) = A_1 e^{s_1 t} + A_2 e^{s_2 t} \tag{4.34}$$

in which A_1 and A_2 are arbitrary constants determined by the initial conditions.
Equation (4.33) is usually written as

$$s_{12} = -\alpha \pm \sqrt{(\alpha^2 - \omega_0^2)} \tag{4.35}$$

where

$$\alpha = \frac{R}{2L} \tag{4.36}$$

and

$$\omega_0^2 = \frac{1}{LC} \tag{4.37}$$

There are three types of solution depending upon whether $\alpha > \omega_0$, $\alpha = \omega_0$ or $\alpha < \omega_0$ and these three solutions are called the *overdamped*, the *critically damped* and the *underdamped* solutions, respectively.

The arbitrary constants are determined from the initial conditions. Thus, at $t = 0$, from equation (4.34)

$$(i)_{t=0} = I_0 = A_1 + A_2$$

$$\left(\frac{di}{dt} \right)_{t=0} = -\frac{1}{L} (RI_0 + V_0) = A_1 s_1 + A_2 s_2$$

and two equations exist to determine the two unknowns.

4.6.1   Overdamped case

If the values of the circuit elements are such that

$$R^2 > \frac{4L}{C}$$

then $\alpha > \omega_0$ and, from equation (4.35), both values of s will be real and negative and the current response of the network will be the sum of two decaying exponentials. For the particular initial conditions of no stored energy in the inductance and the capacitance charged to the opposite polarity to that shown in fig. 4.15 (simply to ensure that the current is positive), then from equation (4.34), at $t = 0$,

$$(i)_{t=0} = I_0 = 0$$

and

$$\left(\frac{di}{dt}\right)_{t=0} = -\frac{1}{L}(RI_0 + V_0) = -\frac{1}{L}(R0 + (-V_0))$$

$$= +\frac{V_0}{L}$$

Thus

$$A_1 + A_2 = 0$$

and

$$A_1 s_1 + A_2 s_2 = \frac{V_0}{L}$$

Solving for A_1 and A_2 gives

$$A_1 = \frac{V_0}{L(s_1 - s_2)} \quad \text{and} \quad A_2 = -\frac{V_0}{L(s_1 - s_2)}$$

The response of the circuit is thus

$$i(t) = \frac{V_0}{L(s_1 - s_2)} e^{s_1 t} - \frac{V_0}{L(s_1 - s_2)} e^{s_2 t} \tag{4.38}$$

where

$$s_1 = -\alpha + \sqrt{(\alpha^2 - \omega_0^2)}$$

and

$$s_2 = -\alpha - \sqrt{(\alpha^2 - \omega_0^2)} \tag{4.39}$$

Note that s_1 and s_2 are both negative, $(s_1 - s_2)$ is positive and s_2 is of greater magnitude than s_1.

The response is shown in fig. 4.17. The resultant curve is seen to be the sum of a longer time constant positive exponential and a shorter time constant negative exponential. Thus the characteristic natural response of an overdamped system is a pulse whose rise time is determined by one time constant and whose fall is determined by the other.

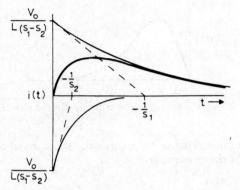

Figure 4.17   Current–time response of overdamped series RLC circuit

4.6.2   Critically damped case

With the particular circuit element values such that

$$R^2 = \frac{4L}{C}$$

then $\alpha = \omega_0$ and from equation (4.35) it is seen that $s_1 = s_2$ and therefore the coefficients of the exponentials of equation (4.38) are infinite and their difference is thus indeterminate. In order to obtain a solution the usual mathematical method is to consider that the difference between s_2 and s_1 is a vanishingly small quantity.

Thus let $s_2 = s_1 + \delta$ where δ is a small increment which is allowed to become zero. Equation (4.38) then becomes

$$i(t) = \frac{V_0}{L}\left(\frac{e^{s_1 t}}{(s_1 - s_1 - \delta)} - \frac{e^{(s_1 + \delta)t}}{(s_1 - s_1 - \delta)}\right)$$

Expanding the exponential term containing δt by a Taylor series gives

$$i(t) = \frac{V_0\, e^{s_1 t}}{L\delta}\left[-1 + \left(1 + \delta t + \frac{(\delta t)^2}{2!} + \ldots\right)\right]$$

$$= \frac{V_0}{L} e^{s_1 t}\left(t + \frac{\delta t^2}{2!} + \ldots\right)$$

If the small increment δ is now allowed to approach zero, so do all the terms in the series in the bracket except the first one and the solution for the current becomes

$$i(t) = \frac{V_0}{L}\, t\, e^{s_1 t}$$

Since from equations (4.39) $s_1 = s_2 = -\alpha$ then

$$i(t) = \frac{V_0}{L}\, t\, e^{-\alpha t}$$

and the response is shown in fig. 4.18.

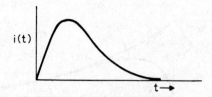

Figure 4.18   Current–time response of critically damped series RLC circuit

The response determined here is for a particular set of initial conditions, and the more general form of the response is

$$i(t) = e^{-\alpha t}(A_1 + A_2 t) \tag{4.40}$$

where A_1 and A_2 are determined from the initial conditions.

4.6.3   Underdamped case

If the resistance of the network of fig. 4.15 is low then so is the energy dissipation. Under these conditions the circuit may become oscillatory and it is said to be under-damped. There is then a continual interchange of stored energy between the inductance and the capacitance.

If $R^2 < 4L/C$ then $\omega_0 > \alpha$ and the values of s_1 and s_2 become conjugate complex numbers. Thus

$$s_1 = -\alpha + j\sqrt{(\omega_0^2 - \alpha^2)} = -\alpha + j\omega_d \tag{4.41}$$

and

$$s_2 = -\alpha - j\sqrt{(\omega_0^2 - \alpha^2)} = -\alpha - j\omega_d \tag{4.42}$$

Equation (4.38) thus becomes

$$i(t) = \frac{V_0}{L}\left(\frac{e^{-\alpha t}\, e^{+j\omega_d t}}{j2\omega_d} - \frac{e^{-\alpha t}\, e^{-j\omega_d t}}{j2\omega_d} \right)$$

$$= \frac{V_0\, e^{-\alpha t}}{\omega_d L}\left(\frac{e^{+j\omega_d t} - e^{-j\omega_d t}}{j2} \right)$$

The mathematical equivalence known as Euler's Theorem states that

$$e^{j\theta} = \cos\theta + j\sin\theta$$

and a corollary of this is that

$$\sin\theta = \frac{e^{j\theta} - e^{-j\theta}}{j2}$$

The expression for the current may therefore be written as

$$i(t) = \frac{V_0}{\omega_d L}\, e^{-\alpha t} \sin\omega_d t \tag{4.43}$$

and the response of a typical underdamped circuit is shown in fig. 4.19.

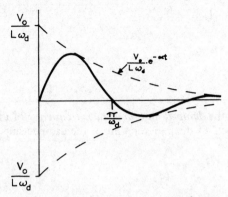

Figure 4.19   Current–time response of underdamped series RLC circuit

Again the response here is for a particular set of initial conditions. The more general form of the response is

$$i(t) = e^{-\alpha t}(A_1 \sin \omega_d t + A_2 \cos \omega_d t) \qquad (4.44)$$

where A_1 and A_2 are unknown constants to be determined from the initial conditions. An alternative form of the general response is

$$i(t) = A_3\, e^{-\alpha t} \sin(\omega_d t + \phi) \qquad (4.45)$$

where A_3 and ϕ are the unknown constants.

4.6.4   Zero damping case

From the analysis of section 4.6.3 it is possible to determine the natural response of an LC circuit. Here $R = 0$ and therefore $\alpha = 0$ and the general response becomes

$$i(t) = A_1 \cos \omega_0 t + A_2 \sin \omega_0 t \qquad (4.46)$$

or

$$i(t) = A_3 \sin(\omega_0 t + \phi) \qquad (4.47)$$

where

$$\omega_0 = \frac{1}{\sqrt{(LC)}}$$

The natural response of the circuit is therefore seen to be a continuous oscillation at an angular frequency of ω_0 rad s^{-1}.

4.6.5   Definitions

The coefficients employed in the analysis of the preceding section may be defined in terms of the responses obtained.

From equation (4.36) $\alpha = R/2L$ and α is defined as the *damping constant*. The damping constant has been shown to be the reciprocal of the time constant of the envelope of the underdamped response.

From equation (4.41)

$$\omega_d^2 = \omega_0^2 - \alpha^2$$

thus

$$\omega_d^2 = \frac{1}{LC} - \frac{R^2}{4L}$$

and ω_d is defined as the *damped natural angular frequency* of the underdamped case. It is the reciprocal of the periodic time of the damped sine wave response of the underdamped case.

From equation (4.37)

$$\omega_0^2 = \frac{1}{LC}$$

and ω_0 is defined as the *undamped natural angular frequency*. It is the reciprocal of the periodic time of the continuous sine wave response of the undamped case when the resistance becomes zero.

4.7   Step response of second-order networks

The total response of an *RLC* circuit to an external stimulus consists of two parts: the natural response of the circuit discussed in section 4.6 which corresponds to the complementary function of the differential equation describing the circuit, and the steady-state solution corresponding to the particular integral of the differential equation describing the behaviour of the circuit.

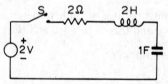

Figure 4.20   Series *RLC* circuit excited by a step input of voltage

Consider the circuit of fig. 4.20. The inductance and capacitance initially contain no energy and a step input of voltage is obtained by closing the switch. Here

$$\alpha = \frac{R}{2L} = \frac{1}{2} = 0.5$$

$$\omega_0 = \frac{1}{\sqrt{(LC)}} = \frac{1}{\sqrt{2}} = 0.707$$

and therefore $\omega_0 > \alpha$ and the circuit is underdamped. Therefore

$$\omega_d^2 = \omega_0^2 - \alpha^2$$

$$= \tfrac{1}{4}$$

and

$$\omega_d = 0.5$$

The initial conditions are

$$(i)_{t=0} = 0$$

(the inductance behaves as an open circuit) and

$$\left(\frac{di}{dt}\right)_{t=0} = \frac{V}{L}$$

(from the application of Kirchhoff's voltage law at $t = 0$), thus

$$\left(\frac{di}{dt}\right)_{t=0} = 1$$

The steady-state response (that is at $t = \infty$) is

$$(i)_{t=\infty} = 0$$

(the capacitance acts as an open circuit).

The solution may be written in either of the general forms given in section 4.6.3. Thus

$$i(t) = A_3 \, e^{-\alpha t} \sin(\omega_d t + \phi).$$

At time $t = 0$, $i = 0$, thus

$$0 = A_3 \sin \phi$$

and ϕ must be zero for a non-trivial solution and thus

$$i(t) = A_3 \, e^{-\alpha t} \sin \omega_d t$$

Also at time $t = 0$,

$$\frac{di}{dt} = \frac{V}{L}$$

and therefore

$$\left(\frac{di}{dt}\right)_{t=0} = \omega_d A_3 = \frac{V}{L}$$

Therefore

$$\omega_d A_3 = \frac{V}{L}$$

and

$$A_3 = \frac{V}{\omega_d L}$$

The complete solution is therefore

$$i(t) = \frac{V}{\omega_d L} e^{-\alpha t} \sin \omega_d t$$

and

$$i(t) = 2\,e^{-t/2}\,\sin 0.5\,t$$

which is illustrated in fig. 4.21.

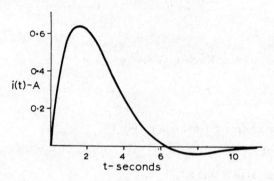

Figure 4.21   Current–time response of the circuit of fig. 4.20

4.8   Q-factor

The Q-factor of a circuit is a measure of how oscillatory its response is to a disturbance. It has been shown that a resistanceless LC circuit will continue to oscillate indefinitely when it has been disturbed. Physical circuits do contain resistance, however, and the Q-factor is a measure of how quickly the oscillations of a physical circuit die away when it has been disturbed.

By definition

$$Q = 2\pi \cdot \frac{\text{maximum stored energy per cycle}}{\text{energy dissipated per cycle}} \qquad (4.48)$$

Referred to the quantities of section 4.6.5 the quality-factor may be shown to be

$$Q = \frac{\omega_0}{2\alpha} \qquad (4.49)$$

and

$$Q = \frac{\omega_0 L}{R} \qquad (4.50)$$

for a series LCR circuit.

Problems

4.1   In the circuit of fig. 4.22 the 2 F capacitance is charged to potential of 6 V and the 1 F capacitance is uncharged. What is the energy stored in the circuit?

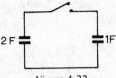

Figure 4.22

Determine the potential on each capacitance and the total stored energy after the switch has been closed for some time. If the final stored energy differs from the initial stored energy explain the discrepancy.

4.2   At $t = 0$ the switch in the circuit of fig. 4.23 is opened. Determine the initial and final values of the voltages and currents of the inductances and capacitances. Construct the nodal equations of the circuit for $t > 0$ assuming that none of the elements possess stored energy for $t \leqslant 0$.

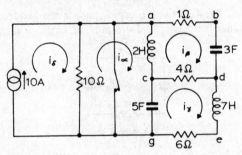

Figure 4.23

4.3   In the circuit shown in fig. 4.24 none of the capacitances and inductances contain any stored energy before the switch is closed at time $t = 0$. (a) What are the

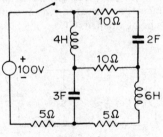

Figure 4.24

voltages and currents of the capacitances and inductances at time $t = 0$? (b) What are the voltages and currents of the capacitances and inductances at time $t = \infty$? (c) Write down the mesh equations for the circuit.

4.4   Write down the mesh equations for the circuit of fig. 4.23 for $t > 0$ if none of the inductances and capacitances possess energy before the switch is opened.

4.5   The application of Kirchhoff's current law to the nodes of a network results in the following node voltage equations

$$3v_a + 6\frac{dv_a}{dt} + \frac{1}{2}\int_0^t v_a\, dt - \frac{1}{2}\int_0^t v_b\, dt - 2\frac{dv_b}{dt} - v_b = 20$$

$$\frac{4}{3}v_b + 5\frac{dv_b}{dt} + \frac{1}{2}\int_0^t v_b\, dt - \frac{1}{2}\int_0^t v_a\, dt - \frac{2dv_a}{dt} - v_a = 3$$

(a) Draw the circuit diagram of the network; (b) draw the circuit diagram of the dual network of the given network; (c) write down the node voltage equations of the dual network.

4.6   In the circuit of fig. 4.25 the 2 F capacitance is charged to a potential of 6 V and the 1 F capacitance is uncharged. Determine an expression for the voltage

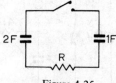

Figure 4.25

across the 1 F capacitance after the switch is closed. Why is this voltage not zero at $t = \infty$? Determine the initial energy, the final energy and the energy dissipated by the resistance. Compare with the answers of problem 1..

4.7   Determine numerical expressions for the source voltages as functions of time and sketch the source voltage–time curves for the circuits shown in fig. 4.26 consequent upon the switches being opened. Give some indication of scale in your sketches.

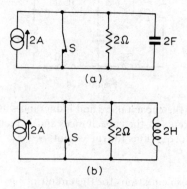

Figure 4.26

4.8 In the circuit shown in fig. 4.27 the 3 F capacitance is uncharged and the switch S has been in position 1 for sufficient time to allow the circuit variables to reach a steady state. (a) What is the current in the 3 Ω resistance? (b) What is the

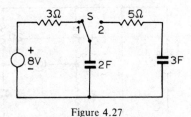

Figure 4.27

voltage on the 2 F capacitance? At time $t = 0$, the switch S is thrown to position 2. (c) Determine the current in the 5 Ω resistance as a function of time; (d) what is the final value of the voltage on the 2 F capacitance?

4.9 A current source has the value $I = 0$ for $t < 0$ and $t > 1$ s, and $I = 10$ A for $0 \leqslant t \leqslant 1$ s. The source is connected to the circuit of fig. 4.28. (a) Determine expressions for the source voltage as functions of time; (b) determine the voltage across the conductance at $t = 1$, 2 and 10 seconds. Sketch the voltage–time curve.

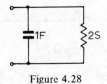

Figure 4.28

4.10 In fig. 4.29 r represents the leakage resistance of a capacitor of capacitance C. The capacitor is connected in series with a constant voltage source V, a resistance R and a switch S as shown. If $C = 2$ F, $R = 2$ Ω and $V = 8$ V determine an expression

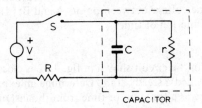

CAPACITOR

Figure 4.29

for the voltage existing on the capacitor after the switch is closed for the following conditions: (a) $r = 6$ Ω (that is, a leaky capacitor); (b) $r = \infty$ (that is, a perfect capacitor). Sketch the capacitor voltage/time curves to a common base for the two conditions and give some indication of scale on the sketch.

4.11   In the circuit shown in fig. 4.30, G is an ideal resistanceless ammeter and C is a variable capacitance. If C is set to a value of 2 F and the switch S is opened at time $t = 0$, determine (a) the current through the ammeter as a function of time;

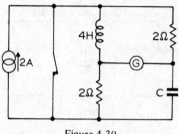

Figure 4.30

(b) the time taken for the current through the ammeter to reach a maximum value and, (c) the maximum value of the current passing through the ammeter. (d) Determine the value of C for which no current will pass through the ammeter after the switch is opened.

4.12   In the circuit shown in fig. 4.31, S is a switch. Determine (a) the voltage between the points A and B immediately after the switch has been closed; (b) the voltage between the points A and B after the switch has been closed for a sufficient

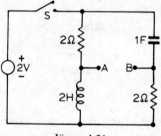

Figure 4.31

time to allow all the currents in the circuit to have reached a steady-state; (c) the maximum value of the voltage between points A and B; (d) the voltage between points A and B as a function of time.

4.13   The switch S in the circuit shown in fig. 4.32 is closed after the remainder of the circuit has attained a steady-state. Determine an expression for the voltage across the capacitance as a function of time from the instant of closing the switch.

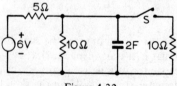

Figure 4.32

4.14   The switch in fig. 4.33 is opened at time $t = 0$ when there is no energy stored in the circuit. (a) Determine, and plot, the resultant source voltage–time function;

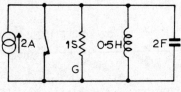

Figure 4.33

(b) what is the Q-factor of the circuit? (c) what is the value of G which will give critical damping?

4.15   Determine functions of time for the currents i_1 and i_2 of fig. 4.34 consequent upon the switch being closed. What are the initial and final values of the currents?

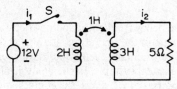

Figure 4.34

5

Steady-State Sinusoidal Response of Networks

Sinusoidal functions of time occur frequently and naturally in many physical systems. They play a large part in the operation, analysis and design of electrical systems of all types and therefore many techniques have been developed to deal with their application to electrical systems. In the analysis of section 4.6 they occurred in the natural responses of LC and RLC circuits and it is therefore to be expected that the response of electrical networks in general will contain sinusoidal functions. A further important reason for concentrating on sinusoidal functions of time is that both the derivatives and integrals of sinusoids are themselves sinusoids and therefore a sinusoidal stimulus will produce sinusoidal responses in a linear network. Furthermore, other types of periodic waves, such as square waves, may be represented by a series of sinusoidal components by Fourier analysis and therefore methods used to analyse the response of a network to a sinusoidal response may be used to predict its response to other types of periodic functions.

This chapter deals with the steady-state response of RLC networks to sinusoidal stimuli. If the response of the network to a suddenly applied sinusoid is required then the steady-state response of this section may be combined with the natural response given by the analysis of section 4.6 to give the total response. Direct solution of circuits using the time-domain methods already covered is discussed initially and their limitations exposed. The special techniques which have been developed to solve this type of problem are then discussed and finally the use of methods of analysis and circuit theorems in the frequency domain is explained.

5.1 Response of series RLC circuit

Consider the circuit of fig. 5.1.

The Kirchhoff voltage law equation is

$$L \frac{di}{dt} + Ri + \frac{1}{C} \int_{-\infty}^{t} i \, dt = V_m \sin \omega t \tag{5.1}$$

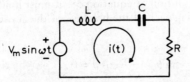

Figure 5.1   Series RLC circuit excited by a sinusoidal voltage

The problem is to determine the current in the circuit when it has attained a steady state, that is after all the transients have been allowed to die away. (As explained in section 4.6, the dual of the above circuit is a parallel GLC circuit excited by a constant current source and hence if the current is determined for the series circuit it is analogous to determining the voltage in the parallel case.)

The steady-state solution corresponds to the particular integral of equation (5.1) and it is logical to assume that the current will be sinusoidal and it will have a general form of

$$i_{ss} = B_1 \sin \omega t + B_2 \cos \omega t \qquad (5.2)$$

or

$$i_{ss} = I_m \sin (\omega t + \theta) \qquad (5.3)$$

where either B_1 and B_2 or I_m and θ are the unknowns to be determined. The steady-state solution must satisfy equation (5.1). The first derivative of equation (5.3) is

$$\frac{d}{dt} (i_{ss}) = I_m \omega \cos (\omega t + \theta) \qquad (5.4)$$

Mathematically the integral of equation 5.3 between the limits $-\infty$ and t is indeterminate.

If, however, it is assumed that at $t = -\infty$, $i_{ss} = 0$ then

$$\int\limits_{-\infty}^{t} i_{ss} \, dt = \int\limits_{-\infty}^{t} I_m \sin (\omega t + \theta) \, dt$$

$$= -\frac{I_m}{\omega} \cos (\omega t + \theta) \qquad (5.5)$$

Substituting equations 5.3, 5.4 and 5.5 into equation 5.1 gives

$$L I_m \omega \cos (\omega t + \theta) + R I_m \sin (\omega t + \theta) - \frac{I_m}{C\omega} \cos (\omega t + \theta) = V_m \sin \omega t$$

Expanding gives

$$\cos \omega t \left(L I_m \omega \cos \theta + R I_m \sin \theta - \frac{I_m}{C\omega} \cos \theta \right)$$

$$- \sin \omega t \left(L I_m \omega \sin \theta - R I_m \cos \theta - \frac{I_m}{C\omega} \sin \theta + V_m \right) = 0$$

If equation 5.3 is a solution of equation 5.1 it must hold for all instants of time and therefore the terms in each of the brackets of the above equation must sum to zero. Therefore

$$LI_m\omega \cos\theta + RI_m \sin\theta - \frac{I_m}{C\omega}\cos\theta = 0$$

and

$$LI_m\omega \sin\theta - RI_m \cos\theta - \frac{I_m}{C\omega}\sin\theta + V_m = 0$$

From the first equation

$$\tan\theta = -\frac{L\omega - (1/C\omega)}{R} \tag{5.6}$$

therefore

$$\sin\theta = -\frac{(\omega L - (1/\omega C))}{\sqrt{\{R^2 + [\omega L - (1/\omega C)]^2\}}}$$

and

$$\cos\theta = \frac{R}{\sqrt{\{R^2 + [\omega L - (1/\omega C)]^2\}}}$$

Substituting into the second equation gives

$$I_m\left(\omega L - \frac{1}{\omega C}\right)\left(\frac{\omega L - (1/\omega C)}{\sqrt{\{R^2 + [\omega L - (1/\omega C)]^2\}}}\right)$$

$$+ I_m \frac{R}{\sqrt{\{R^2 + [\omega L - (1/\omega C)]^2\}}} = V_m$$

Thus

$$I_m \frac{\{R^2 + [\omega L - (1/\omega C)]^2\}}{\sqrt{\{R^2 + [\omega L - (1/\omega C)]^2\}}} = V_m$$

and

$$I_m = \frac{V_m}{\sqrt{\{R^2 + [\omega L - (1/\omega C)]^2\}}} \tag{5.7}$$

Therefore

$$i_{ss} = \frac{V_m}{\sqrt{\{R^2 + [\omega L - (1/\omega C)]^2\}_f}} \sin\left\{\omega t + \tan^{-1}\left(-\left(\frac{\omega L - (1/\omega C)}{R}\right)\right)\right\} \tag{5.8}$$

and

$$i_{ss} = I_m \sin(\omega t + \theta) \tag{5.9}$$

It should be noted that the amplitude of the sinusoidal current response (equation 5.7) is dependent upon R, L and C and upon the angular frequency ω of the forcing voltage.

Similarly the phase of the sinusoidal current response with respect to the phase of the forcing voltage (equation 5.6) is dependent upon R, L and C and upon the frequency of the forcing voltage wave.

5.2   Frequency response

5.2.1   Amplitude

Consider the circuit of fig. 5.1. If the values of R, L, C and V_m remain constant and ω is varied then as stated in equation 5.7 the amplitude of the current will vary. A plot of the variation in the current amplitude with frequency is termed the amplitude frequency response.

Several points should be noted concerning the amplitude response. Equation 5.7 is

$$I_m = \frac{V_m}{\sqrt{\{R^2 + [\omega L - (1/\omega C)]^2\}}}$$

At $\omega = 0$, $I_m = 0$.

At $\omega = \infty$, $I_m = 0$.

At $\omega = \omega_0 = \dfrac{1}{\sqrt{(LC)}}$, $I_m = \dfrac{V_m}{R}$.

ω_0 is termed the *resonant* frequency. At the resonant frequency the circuit behaves as a pure resistance, the current amplitude is a maximum and the voltage and current waves are in phase.

A typical amplitude frequency response for a series RLC circuit is shown in fig. 5.2.

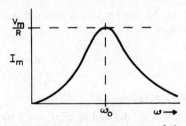

Figure 5.2   Amplitude frequency response of circuit of fig. 5.1

5.2.2   Phase

Consider again the circuit of fig. 5.1 with R, L, C and V_m constant and ω varied. A plot of the variation in the phase difference between the current and voltage sinusoids with frequency is termed the phase frequency response. The phase of the sinusoidal current wave with respect to the supply voltage is given by equation (5.6) as

$$\tan \theta = - \frac{\omega L - (1/\omega C)}{R}$$

Points to be noted concerning the phase response are:

as $\omega \to 0,$ $\theta \to + \dfrac{\pi}{2}$

for

$\omega < \omega_0,$ θ is positive

for

$\omega = \omega_0,$ $\theta = 0$

for

$\omega > \omega_0,$ θ is negative

as

$\omega \to \infty,$ $\theta \to - \dfrac{\pi}{2}$

A typical phase frequency response for a series RLC circuit is shown in fig. 5.3.

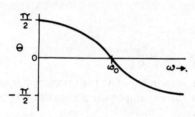

Figure 5.3   Phase frequency response of circuit of fig. 5.2

Analysis of this type will enable the amplitude and phase frequency responses to be plotted for most networks.

5.3 Q-factor, bandwidth and resonance

The Q-factor of a circuit has been defined in section 4.8 by equation (4.48) as

$$Q = 2\pi \times \frac{\text{maximum stored energy per cycle}}{\text{energy dissipated per cycle}}$$

The stored energy in a series RLC circuit is

$$W_s = \tfrac{1}{2}Li^2 + \tfrac{1}{2}Cv_c^2$$

Let

$$i = I_m \sin \omega t$$

then

$$v_c = \frac{1}{C} \int i \, \mathrm{d}t = -\frac{I_m}{\omega C} \cos \omega t$$

and the stored energy is

$$W_s = \tfrac{1}{2} L I_m^2 \sin^2 \omega t + \tfrac{1}{2} \frac{I_m^2}{\omega^2 C} \cos^2 \omega t$$

At the resonant frequency, ω_0, let the current amplitude be I_{mo}. As

$$\omega = \omega_0 = \frac{1}{\sqrt{(LC)}}$$

then

$$W_s = \tfrac{1}{2} L I_{mo}^2 \sin^2 \omega_0 t + \tfrac{1}{2} \frac{I_{mo}^2}{\omega_0^2 C} \cos^2 \omega_0 t$$

$$= \tfrac{1}{2} I_{mo}^2 (L \sin^2 \omega_0 t + L \cos^2 \omega_0 t)$$

$$= \tfrac{1}{2} L I_{mo}^2 \tag{5.10}$$

Thus the stored energy at resonance is constant and independent of time. The energy dissipated per cycle at resonance is

$$W_d = \int\limits_{0}^{2\pi/\omega_0} (I_{mo} \sin \omega_0 t)^2 R \, \mathrm{d}t$$

Solving the integral equation gives

$$W_d = \frac{\pi R I_{mo}^2}{\omega_0} \tag{5.11}$$

Thus

$$Q = 2\pi \frac{W_s}{W_d} = \frac{2\pi \tfrac{1}{2} L I_{mo}^2 \omega_0}{\pi R I_{mo}^2}$$

and, for a series RLC circuit,

$$Q = \frac{\omega_0 L}{R}$$

The Q-factor of any other circuit may be determined by a similar analysis but by the principle of duality, the Q-factor of a parallel GLC circuit is

$$Q = \frac{\omega_0 C}{G}$$

or

$$Q = \omega_0 C R$$

where

$$R = \frac{1}{G}$$

From the expression for the Q-factor of a series RLC circuit it is seen that the Q of the circuit may be changed without changing ω_0 or R. If L and C are changed but with their product remaining constant the shape of the amplitude frequency response will change. Figure 5.4 shows the amplitude response of three series RLC circuits possessing the same ω_0 and R but different Q-factors.

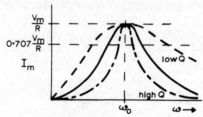

Figure 5.4   Illustration of the variation in amplitude frequency response with Q-factor

It is seen that a high-Q circuit has a 'sharper' or 'peakier' resonance curve and is much more 'selective', that is, the current amplitude is high over only a small range of frequencies. For this reason the Q-factor is sometimes called the 'quality-factor' of a circuit.

Another measure of the sharpness of the resonance curve is the *bandwidth* which is defined in terms of the frequencies at which the power dissipated in the circuit falls to one half of its value at resonance, which is a maximum.

From equation (5.11) the energy dissipated in a series RLC circuit is obviously a maximum at the resonant frequency because the current at that frequency is a maximum. The average power dissipated at resonance will therefore be

$$P_0 = \frac{\text{energy dissipated per cycle}}{\text{periodic time of sine wave}}$$

thus

$$P_0 = W_d \times \frac{\omega_0}{2\pi} = \frac{R I_{mo}^2}{2}$$

But at resonance, from equation (5.7)

$$I_{mo} = \frac{V_m}{R}$$

because

$$\omega_0 L = \frac{1}{\omega_0 C}$$

thus

$$P_0 = \frac{V_m^2}{2R} \qquad (5.12)$$

At any other frequency the power dissipated will be

$$P = \frac{I_m^2 R}{2}$$

From equation (5.7)

$$I_m = \frac{V_m}{\sqrt{\{R^2 + [\omega L - (1/\omega C)]^2\}}}$$

thus

$$P = \frac{R V_m^2}{2\{R^2 + [\omega L - (1/\omega C)]^2\}}$$

Therefore the ratio of this power to the power dissipated at resonance is

$$\frac{P}{P_0} = \frac{1}{\{1 + (1/R^2)[\omega L - (1/\omega C)]^2\}}$$

At the 'half-power points', or frequencies at which the power dissipated is halved, $P/P_0 = \frac{1}{2}$, $I_m/I_{m0} = 1/\sqrt{2} = 0.707$. Therefore

$$1 + \frac{1}{R^2}\left(\omega L - \frac{1}{\omega C}\right)^2 = 2$$

and

$$\left(\omega L - \frac{1}{\omega C}\right) = \pm R$$

Solving for ω gives

$$\omega = \pm \frac{R}{2L} \pm \sqrt{\left\{\left(\frac{R}{2L}\right)^2 + \frac{1}{LC}\right\}} = \pm \frac{\omega_0}{2Q} \pm \sqrt{\left\{\left(\frac{\omega_0}{2Q}\right)^2 + \omega_0^2\right\}} \qquad (5.13)$$

Considering only the positive values of ω which satisfy equation (5.13) then

$$\omega_1 = -\frac{R}{2L} + \sqrt{\left\{\left(\frac{R}{2L}\right)^2 + \frac{1}{LC}\right\}} = -\frac{\omega_0}{2Q} + \sqrt{\left\{\left(\frac{\omega_0}{2Q}\right)^2 + \omega_0^2\right\}}$$

and

$$\omega_2 = +\frac{R}{2L} + \sqrt{\left\{\left(\frac{R}{2L}\right)^2 + \frac{1}{LC}\right\}} = +\frac{\omega_0}{2Q} + \sqrt{\left\{\left(\frac{\omega_0}{2Q}\right)^2 + \omega_0^2\right\}}$$

The bandwidth is defined as

$$B = \omega_2 - \omega_1$$

Thus substituting for ω_1 and ω_2 gives

$$B = \frac{R}{L} = \frac{\omega_0}{Q} \qquad (5.14)$$

It is seen that high Q circuits have smaller bandwidths than low Q circuits and they are therefore more 'selective' in their response.

It should be noted that for high Q circuits

$$\omega_0 L \gg R$$

and thus

$$\omega_0 \gg \frac{R}{L} \qquad \text{or} \qquad \frac{1}{LC} \gg \frac{R^2}{L^2}$$

and from the equation for ω_1 and ω_2

and

$$\left.\begin{array}{l} \omega_1 = \omega_0 - \dfrac{R}{2L} \\[3mm] \\ \omega_2 = \omega_0 + \dfrac{R}{2L} \end{array}\right\} \qquad (5.15)$$

The potential difference across the inductance of a series RLC circuit at resonance is given by

$$v_L = L \frac{di}{dt} = L\omega_0 I_{mo} \cos \omega_0 t$$

Substituting for I_{mo}

$$v_L = V_{mL} \cos \omega_0 t = \frac{V_m}{R} \omega_0 L \cos \omega_0 t \qquad (5.16)$$

Therefore

$$V_{mL} = Q V_m \qquad (5.17)$$

Thus for series RLC circuits where $Q > 1$ the potential difference across both the inductance and capacitance is greater than the source voltage and the circuit is said to provide *voltage magnification*. Obviously, for circuits with Q-factors of several hundred, great magnification can be achieved.

By duality, the magnitudes of the currents flowing in both the capacitance and inductance of a parallel GLC circuit fed by a sinusoidal current source are greater than the source current at resonance for high Q circuits and the circuits are said to provide *current magnification*.

5.4   A.C. quantities

The reasons why alternating rather than direct quantities are used in electrical engineering systems are many and varied. In the generation, transmission and distribution of electrical power, a.c. systems are much more convenient and economical to operate because of the ease with which alternating power may be transformed to a high-voltage level for transmission over long distances and to a low level for use by the consumer. In the field of communications to transmit information via a d.c. system required conductors but a.c. systems may transmit information by the use of electromagnetic waves which require no material path. There are an infinite number of alternating quantities (for example, square waves, triangular waves) which could be used to carry out these tasks but the sinusoidal function is pre-eminent for several reasons. Firstly, it is the most natural, as shown in section 4.6. Secondly its differential and integral are both sinusoids. Thirdly, any other periodic function may be represented by a series of sinusoids, as stated by Fourier. Finally, if an electrical system consists of linear elements then all of the variables are sinusoids if the stimulus is a sinusoid.

5.4.1 Instantaneous, mean and r.m.s. values

Consider a resistance carrying a sinusoidal current. The power dissipated in the resistance is then a function of the time.

The instantaneous value of the current at time t is

$$i = I_m \sin \omega t \tag{5.18}$$

The volt–ampere equation for a resistance is

$$v = iR$$

therefore the instantaneous value of the voltage is

$$v = I_m R \sin \omega t = V_m \sin \omega t \tag{5.19}$$

The power dissipated by the resistance is

$$p = vi$$

therefore the instantaneous power dissipated by the resistance is

$$p = I_m^2 R \sin^2 \omega t$$

and

$$p = \frac{I_m^2 R}{2} (1 - \cos 2\omega t) \tag{5.20}$$

The instantaneous voltage, current and power waves are shown in fig. 5.5 (a), (b) and (c). The instantaneous power is seen to be always positive and to vary at twice the frequency of the current function.

The mean or average level of the power dissipated is seen to be

$$P_{a.c.} = \frac{I_m^2 R}{2}$$

where

$$P_{a.c.} = \frac{1}{T} \int_t^{t+T} p \, dt$$

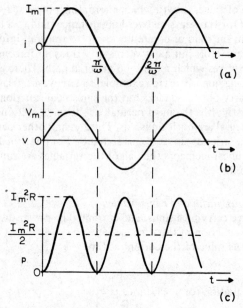

Figure 5.5   Current, voltage and power waveforms for resistance element

where T is the periodic time of the wave. It should be noted that the mean or average values of both the current and voltage are zero.

The mean a.c. power should be compared with the mean d.c. power which is

$$P_{\text{d.c.}} = (I_{\text{d.c.}})^2 R$$

An *effective* current is defined in the a.c. case such that

$$P_{\text{a.c.}} = (I_{\text{effective}})^2 R$$

And thus $(I_{\text{effective}})$ is the a.c. current which will cause the resistance to dissipate the same mean power as a d.c. current of the same magnitude. Therefore

$$(I_{\text{effective}})^2 R = \frac{1}{T} \int_t^{t+T} \frac{I_m^2 R}{2} (1 - \cos 2\omega t) \, dt$$

and

$$I_{\text{effective}} = \sqrt{\left\{ \frac{1}{T} \int_t^{t+T} \frac{I_m^2}{2} (1 - \cos 2\omega t) \, dt \right\}}$$

In order to find $I_{\text{effective}}$ it is therefore necessary to square the current, take its mean, and then take the square-root of the mean square. Thus $I_{\text{effective}}$ is called the root-mean-square current or

$$I_{\text{effective}} = I_{\text{r.m.s.}} \qquad (5.21)$$

Thus

$$I_{r.m.s.} = \frac{I_m}{\sqrt{2}}$$

(5.22)

or

$$I_{r.m.s.} = 0.707 \, I_m$$

It should be noted that these relationships hold for *sinusoids* only. The r.m.s. value of a square-wave is equal to the amplitude of the wave and the r.m.s. value of a triangular wave is $1/\sqrt{3}$ of the amplitude.

The relationships between the r.m.s. values of the current and voltage and the mean a.c. power may be derived from the mean power expression, that is

$$P_{a.c.} = \frac{I_m^2 R}{2}$$

As

$$V_m = I_m R$$

then

$$P_{a.c.} = \frac{V_m}{\sqrt{2}} \times \frac{I_m}{\sqrt{2}}$$

Thus

$$P_{a.c.} = V_{r.m.s.} \, I_{r.m.s.}$$

$$P_{a.c.} = \frac{(V_{r.m.s.})^2}{R}$$

(5.23)

and

$$P_{a.c.} = (I_{r.m.s.})^2 R$$

It is usual practice in a.c. circuit theory to use r.m.s. values for sinusoidal quantities whenever possible and the suffix 'r.m.s.' is usually not used. It is understood, therefore, that a single capital letter such as I representing a sinusoidally varying quantity refers to the r.m.s. value of that quantity. Henceforth all references to quantities such as current or voltage may be taken to refer to r.m.s. values unless otherwise stated.

Thus a current

$$i = I_m \sin \omega t$$

will be referred to as I and it is understood that

$$I = \frac{I_m}{\sqrt{2}}$$

If a sinusoidally varying current is said to have a value of, say, 5 A it may be taken to be the r.m.s. value of the current.

5.4.2   Real and reactive power

Inductive circuits

Consider an inductance carrying a sinusoidal current. If the current is

$$i = I_m \sin \omega t$$

then, as the volt–ampere equation of the inductance is

$$v = L \frac{di}{dt}$$

$$v = \omega L I \cos \omega t = V_m \cos \omega t$$

where

$$V_m = I_m \omega L.$$

The instantaneous power is

$$p = vi = V_m I_m \cos \omega t \sin \omega t$$

and

$$p = VI \sin 2\omega t$$

The current, voltage and power functions are shown in fig. 5.6(a), (b) and (c).

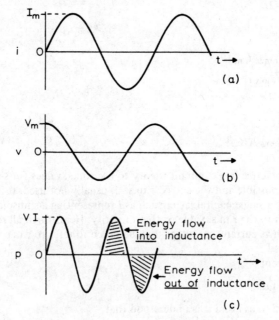

Figure 5.6   Current, voltage and power waveforms for inductance element

The power is again seen to vary at twice the frequency of the current but the mean power is seen to be zero. For half the time energy flows into the inductance and for half the time it flows out again.

The peak of the fluctuating component is called the *reactive power Q*.
For the inductance

$$Q = VI$$

or

$$Q = \frac{V^2}{\omega L}$$

(5.24)

or

$$Q = I^2 \omega L$$

It should be noted that the phase difference between the current and voltage sinusoids is $\pi/2$ radians and the current is said to lag the voltage by 90°.

Consider now a series RL circuit carrying a current of $i = I_m \sin \omega t$ amperes. The voltages across the resistance and inductance are

$$v_R = I_m R \sin \omega t$$

and

$$v_L = I_m \omega L \cos \omega t$$

The total voltage across the combination is

$$v = v_R + v_L = I_m (R \sin \omega t + \omega L \cos \omega t)$$

Therefore

$$v = I_m \sqrt{(R^2 + \omega^2 L^2)} \sin (\omega t + \phi)$$

where

$$\tan \phi = \frac{\omega L}{R}$$

(5.25)

Let

$$V_m = I_m \sqrt{(R^2 + \omega^2 L^2)}$$

(5.26)

then the instantaneous power is

$$p = vi = V_m I_m \sin \omega t \sin (\omega t + \phi)$$

Therefore

$$p = \frac{V_m I_m}{2} \cos \phi - \frac{V_m I_m}{2} \cos (2\omega t + \phi)$$

and

$$p = VI \cos \phi - VI \cos (2\omega t + \phi)$$

The mean power is, therefore,

$$P = VI \cos \phi$$

(5.27)

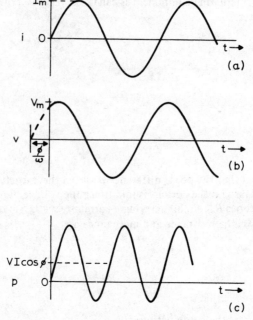

Figure 5.7   Current, voltage and power waveforms for a series RL circuit

The factor $\cos \phi$ is called the *power factor*. For the RL circuit the current *lags* the voltage by ϕ and the circuit is said to possess a *lagging power-factor*.

The voltage, current and power functions are shown in fig. 5.7 (a), (b) and (c).

Capacitive circuits

Consider a capacitance with a sinusoidal voltage applied to it of

$$v = V_m \sin \omega t$$

The volt–ampere equation of the capacitance is

$$i = C \frac{dv}{dt}$$

therefore

$$i = V_m \omega C \cos \omega t = I_m \cos \omega t$$

and the instantaneous power is

$$p = vi = V_m I_m \cos \omega t \sin \omega t$$

Therefore

$$p = VI \sin 2\omega t$$

The mean power is thus zero, that is

$$P = 0$$

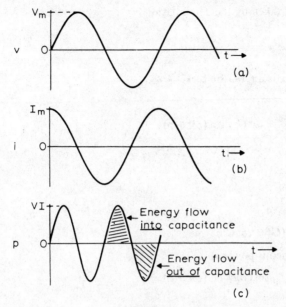

Figure 5.8   Current, voltage and power waveforms for capacitance element

The voltage, current and power functions are shown in fig. 5.8 (a), (b) and (c).

The power function is again of twice the frequency of the voltage function and again, for half of the time energy flows into the capacitance and for half the time it flows out again. The reactive power is

$$Q = -VI$$

or

$$Q = -V^2 \omega C$$

$$\left.\begin{array}{c} \\ \\ \\ \\ \\ \end{array}\right\} \qquad (5.28)$$

or

$$Q = -\frac{I^2}{\omega C}$$

The convention adopted is that reactive power associated with an inductance is positive whilst that associated with a capacitance is negative.

It should be noted that the phase difference between the current and the voltage is $\pi/2$ radians and the current is said to *lead* the voltage by 90°.

Consider now a parallel GC circuit with an applied voltage of

$$v = V_m \sin \omega t$$

The currents in the capacitance and conductance are

$$i_C = V_m C \cos \omega t$$

and

$$i_G = V_m G \sin \omega t$$

The total current taken by the combination is

$$i = i_C + i_G$$

that is

$$i = V_m(\omega C \cos \omega t + G \sin \omega t)$$

Therefore

$$i = V_m \sqrt{(G^2 + \omega^2 C^2)} \sin (\omega t + \phi)$$

where

$$\tan \phi = \frac{\omega C}{G} \tag{5.29}$$

Let

$$I_m = V_m \sqrt{(G^2 + \omega^2 C^2)} \tag{5.30}$$

then the instantaneous power is

$$p = vi = V_m I_m \sin (\omega t) \sin (\omega t + \phi)$$

Therefore

$$p = \frac{V_m I_m}{2} \cos \phi - \frac{V_m I_m}{2} \cos (2\omega t + \phi)$$

and

$$p = VI \cos \phi - VI \cos (2\omega t + \phi)$$

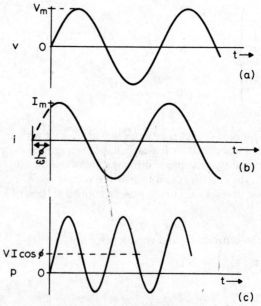

Figure 5.9   Current, voltage and power waveforms for a parallel RC circuit

The mean power is

$$P = VI \cos \phi$$

For the *GC* circuit, the current *leads* the voltage by ϕ and the circuit is said to possess a *leading power factor*. The voltage, current and power functions are shown in fig. 5.9 (a), (b) and (c).

5.5 Representation of sinusoids

The total response of *RLC* networks to various types of stimuli has been discussed in chapter 4 and some aspects of the steady-state response of such networks to sinusoidal stimuli has been discussed in section 5.1. The response of electrical systems of all types to steady-state sinusoidal stimuli is of particular importance and the differential equation approach discussed in section 5.1, whilst rigorous and powerful, is cumbersome, wasteful and unnecessary.

Several special techniques have been developed to facilitate the rapid, efficient and accurate analysis of electrical systems excited by steady-state sinusoidal stimuli and this section introduces two of the most useful of these. They are based upon the rotating vector representation of sine-waves which results in a phasor diagram and the complex number representation which results in the Argand diagram.

The result of both of these methods is to convert a network from the time domain, in which the variables and some of the volt–ampere equations are functions of time, into the frequency domain, where the variables are not functions of time and some of the volt–ampere equations are functions of frequency. The frequency-domain methods reduce steady-state sinusoidal problems to forms which are similar to those used for resistive networks.

5.5.1   Rotating vectors
The simplest way of producing a sine wave of voltage is to rotate a rectangular coil at a constant angular velocity in a uniform magnetic field as shown in fig. 5.10.

The voltage induced in a conductor moving with respect to a magnetic field is given by the product

$$v = (Bl) \times (u)$$

where the conductor, of length l, is at all times perpendicular to the field and u is the velocity of the conductor perpendicularly across the field. Thus the voltage generated in the coil of figure 5.10 is

$$v = 2Bl\omega r \cos \theta$$

and

$$v = 2Bl\omega r \cos \omega t$$

and

$$v = V_m \cos \theta \qquad \text{(where } V_m \text{ is a constant)}$$

This is the basic principle of operation of alternators and the pictorial plot of the sine wave produced is shown in fig. 5.10.

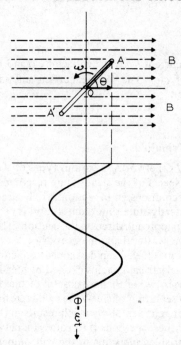

Figure 5.10   Voltage–time waveform for coil rotating in a magnetic field

The projection of the coil side OA onto the horizontal axis, at any instant of time t is

$OA \cos \theta$

or

$OA \cos \omega t$

and therefore 'the voltage generated in the coil may be represented by the projection of the coil side on to the horizontal axis'.

This is the basis of the representation of a sine wave by a rotating vector.

Consider fig. 5.11 where the rotating vector of magnitude V_m represents the amplitude of the voltage generated in the coil of fig. 5.10.

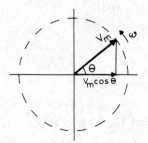

Figure 5.11   Rotating vector

The tip of the vector traverses the circular locus shown and the projection of the vector onto the horizontal axis at time t is

$$v = V_m \cos \theta$$

or

$$v = V_m \cos \omega t$$

which is the instantaneous value of the voltage generated in the coil. If the coil is connected to some circuit such that a current flows given by

$$i = I_m \cos (\omega t - \phi)$$

then this may be represented by another rotating vector of magnitude I_m but displaced by a constant angle ϕ from the vector V_m as shown in fig. 5.12.

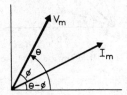

Figure 5.12   Rotating vector for current and voltage

The projection of the current vector on to the horizontal axis is

$$i = I_m \cos (\theta - \phi)$$

or

$$i = I_m \cos (\omega t - \phi)$$

which is the instantaneous current at time t.

It may be seen that in electrical networks excited by a single steady-state sinusoidal excitation function all of the currents and voltages in the network will be of the same frequency but of differing phases. Thus they may all be represented as vectors rotating at the same velocity and keeping their relative amplitudes and phases with time.

A further simplification is to consider that all the vectors remain stationary but the reference axis rotates in the opposite direction at the angular speed of ω radians per second. The projections of the vectors on to the rotating axis have exactly the same value as before. The stationary vectors are then said to be *phasors* and a typical *phasor diagram* which exists in the frequency domain is shown in fig. 5.13(a). In many a.c. problems the relative magnitudes and phases of the variables are more important than their instantaneous values and therefore the rotating reference axis is omitted. Phasors and phasor diagrams are seen to be time independent quantities representing time varying ones and they are thus frequency domain quantities. The act of bringing the rotating vector diagram to a halt and rotating the reference axis and then omitting the reference axis transforms the circuit variables from the time domain to the frequency domain.

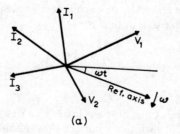

(a)

Figure 5.13(a)   Typical phasor diagram

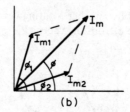

(b)

Figure 5.13(b)   Illustration of phasor addition

Phasor addition and subtraction

Mathematical operations on sinusoidal functions can be accomplished by operations on the corresponding phasors in the frequency domain. Since the phasors are vectors they may be added and subtracted by the usual vector methods. Consider the addition of two currents, say

$$i = i_1 + i_2$$

Let

$$i_1 = I_{m1} \cos(\omega t + \phi_1)$$

and

$$i_2 = I_{m2} \cos(\omega t + \phi_2)$$

The phasors representing i_1 and i_2 are shown in fig. 5.13(b) together with their vector sum. Thus

$$i = I_m \cos(\omega t + \phi)$$

In order to express I_m and ϕ in terms of I_{m1}, I_{m2}, ϕ_1 and ϕ_2 the projections of phasors I_{m1} and I_{m2} on to the horizontal and vertical axis must be taken and summed to give the components of phasor I_m. Thus

$$(I_m)_{\text{Vertical Component}} = I_{m1} \sin \phi_1 + I_{m2} \sin \phi_2$$

and

$$(I_m)_{\text{Horizontal Component}} = I_{m1} \cos \phi_1 + I_{m2} \cos \phi_2$$

then

$$I_m = \sqrt{\{(I_m)_{\text{VC}}^2 + (I_m)_{\text{HC}}^2\}}$$

and

$$I_m = \sqrt{\{(I_{m1}\sin\phi_1 + I_{m2}\sin\phi_2)^2 + (I_{m1}\cos\phi_1 + I_{m2}\cos\phi_2)^2\}} \tag{5.31}$$

Also

$$\tan\phi = \frac{(I_m)_{VC}}{(I_m)_{HC}} = \frac{I_{m1}\sin\phi_1 + I_{m2}\sin\phi_2}{I_{m1}\cos\phi_1 + I_{m2}\cos\phi_2} \tag{5.32}$$

The phasor I_m may then be expressed as

$$I_m = |I_m|\underline{/\phi} \tag{5.33}$$

which is read as 'magnitude of I_m at an angle of ϕ.

In order to specify a phasor completely *both* the magnitude and phase angle must be quoted.

Integration and differentiation

Phasors represent functions of time and therefore the operations of differentiation and integration on the time functions will change both the magnitudes and phases of the phasors. Consider the current

$$i = I_m \cos(\omega t + \phi)$$

The differential is

$$\frac{di}{dt} = -I_m \sin(\omega t + \phi)$$

or

$$\frac{di}{dt} = +I_m \cos(\omega t + \phi + 90°)$$

and therefore the phasor magnitude has been multiplied by ω and its phase has been advanced by 90°. Similarly

$$\int i\, dt = \frac{1}{\omega} I_m \cos(\omega t + \phi - 90°)$$

and here the phasor magnitude has been divided by ω and its phase retarded by 90°.

The three phasors representing

$$i, \qquad \frac{di}{dt} \qquad \text{and} \qquad \int i\, dt$$

are shown in fig. 5.14.

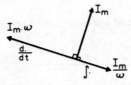

Figure 5.14 Illustration of the phasor representation of the integral and differential of a current

5.5.2   *Complex number representation of sinusoids*

The rotating vector method of representing sine waves and the resulting phasor diagram gives a good visual representation of the relationships between the variables in a network. The vector algebra which is required to analyse networks is, however, as illustrated in section 5.5.1, cumbersome and unwieldy and consists essentially of 'squaring' and 'taking roots'. A much simpler method of analysing networks results from the representation of a phasor as a complex number.

A phasor may be drawn as a two-dimensional vector on a phasor diagram; a complex number may be represented as a point or line on the Argand diagram. There is thus a direct analogy between a phasor and a complex number and one may be used to represent the other. The basis for the representation of a complex number on the Argand diagram is Euler's identity which is[†]

$$e^{\pm j\theta} = \cos \theta \pm j \sin \theta \tag{5.34}$$

and its corollaries

$$\cos \theta = \tfrac{1}{2}(e^{j\theta} + e^{-j\theta}) \tag{5.35}$$

and

$$\sin \theta = -j/2(e^{j\theta} - e^{-j\theta}) \tag{5.36}$$

From equation (5.34) the quantity $e^{j\theta}$ may be thought of as being a vector of unit length which has resolved components of $\cos \theta$ and $\sin \theta$ on the horizontal and vertical axes respectively and thus makes an angle θ with the horizontal axis. The horizontal and vertical axes then correspond to the real and imaginary axes of the Argand diagram or the complex plane. On the Argand diagram complex numbers are plotted with their real parts along the horizontal or real axis and their imaginary parts on the vertical or imaginary axis. The unit vector representing $e^{j\theta}$ is shown plotted on the complex plane in fig. 5.15.

The quantity $e^{-j\theta}$ is a similar unit vector which stands at an angle of $-\theta$ from the real axis as shown in fig. 5.15.

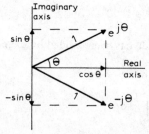

Figure 5.15   Representation of the quantities $e^{j\theta}$ and $e^{-j\theta}$ on the Argand diagram

A phasor of magnitude I_m and phase ϕ may be represented on the complex plane by the quantity

$$I_m = |I_m| e^{j\theta} \tag{5.37}$$

[†] j here is equivalent to the i used by mathematicians to signify $\sqrt{(-1)}$; j tends to be used by electrical engineers to avoid confusion with *i* denoting the instantaneous value of a current.

because both conditions are satisfied for representing the phasor as a two-dimensional vector, that is, the quantity $e^{j\theta}$ sets the vector at the correct angle ϕ to the horizontal axis and the length of the unit vector is multiplied by $|I_m|$ to obtain a vector of the correct length. In order to obtain the function of time represented by equation (5.37) it is again necessary to rotate the vector and to take its projection on to the real axis.

From equation (5.34) an additional expression is

$$\cos \theta = \text{Re}[e^{j\theta}] \tag{5.38}$$

where Re is read as 'the real part of'. Equation (5.38) leads to a further explanation of the meaning of equation (5.37).

Consider the current

$$i = I_m \cos(\omega t + \phi)$$

which is a time domain expression.

Substituting for the cosine function from equation (5.38) gives

$$i = I_m\{\text{Re}[e^{j(\omega t+\phi)}]\}$$

and since I_m is a real quantity

$$i = \text{Re}[I_m e^{j(\omega t+\phi)}] \tag{5.39}$$

or

$$i = \text{Re}[(I_m e^{j\theta}) e^{j\omega t}] \tag{5.40}$$

Equation (5.40) is a time-domain expression which states that a phasor represented by $(I_m e^{j\phi})$ is rotated at an angular velocity ω and in order to find the instantaneous value of the current Re states that the projection on to the real axis must be taken. Thus the $(e^{j\omega t})$ term signifies rotation and in order to bring the phasor to rest and hence to convert it from a time domain quantity to a frequency domain one the $(e^{j\omega t})$ term is omitted. The term $(I_m e^{j\phi})$ is thus a *complex number*[†] which represents the frequency domain phasor and it may be written as

$$\mathbf{I_m} = I_m e^{j\phi} \tag{5.41}$$

If it is required to obtain the function of time which a phasor represents then the reverse procedure must be adopted. Firstly the phasor is multiplied by $(e^{j\omega t})$ and then the real part of the resulting quantity is taken, that is

$$i = \text{Re}[\mathbf{I_m} e^{j\omega t}]$$
$$= \text{Re}[|I_m| e^{j\phi} e^{j\omega t}]$$

where $|I_m|$ means 'the modulus of the complex number $\mathbf{I_m}$' and thus

$$i = |I_m| \cos(\omega t + \phi)$$

† Complex numbers are written in bold type, thus $\mathbf{I_m}$.

Manipulation of complex phasors

Complex phasors may be quoted in two forms. For some types of operation it is more convenient to use one form than the other. Consider a current which is represented in the time domain as

$$i = I_m \cos(\omega t + \phi)$$

In the frequency domain this is represented by a complex phasor of modulus I_m and phase ϕ. The *polar* form of the phasor is

$$I_m = |I_m|\, e^{j\phi}$$

or

$$I_m = |I_m|\underline{/\phi}$$

The *rectangular form* of the same phasor in the complex plane is

$$I_m = I_{rm} + jI_{im}$$

where I_{rm} and I_{im} are the projections on the real and imaginary axis respectively. Thus

$$I_{rm} = |I_m| \cos \phi$$

and

$$I_{im} = |I_m| \sin \phi$$

It is obvious that, to convert from one form of the phasor to the other, one uses the relationships

$$|I_m| = \sqrt{\{(I_{rm})^2 + (I_{im})^2\}}$$

and

$$\tan \phi = \frac{I_{im}}{I_{rm}}$$

Consider the two current phasors[†]

$$I_1 = |I_1|\, e^{j\phi_1}$$

and

$$I_2 = |I_2|\, e^{j\phi_2}$$

The sum of the currents is most easily determined by using the rectangular form of the phasors. Therefore

$$I = I_1 + I_2$$

and

$$I_r + jI_i = I_{r1} + jI_{i1} + I_{r2} + jI_{i2}$$

[†] Again it is usual for the modulus of a complex phasor to be the r.m.s. value of the quantity that it represents. Thus, here, the phasors carry no subscript 'm' and they may be taken to have moduli equal to the r.m.s. values of the quantities represented.

Therefore

$$I_r = I_{r1} + I_{r2}$$

and

$$I_i = I_{i1} + I_{i2}$$

Similarly the difference between the two phasors is best found using the rectangular form.

Consider a voltage phasor V and a current phasor I such that

$$V = |V| e^{j\phi_1}$$

and

$$I = |I| e^{j\phi_2}$$

To find the product of the two phasors it is better to consider the polar form of the phasors.

Thus if

$$M = VI$$

then

$$M = (|V| e^{j\phi_1})(|I| e^{j\phi_2})$$

and

$$M = |V||I| e^{j(\phi_1 + \phi_2)}$$

It should be noted that the magnitude of M is given by the *product* of the magnitudes of the constituent phasors whilst the phase of M is given by the *sum* of the phases of the constituent phasors.

Similarly if

$$Z = \frac{V}{I}$$

then

$$Z = \frac{|V| e^{j\phi_1}}{|I| e^{j\phi_2}}$$

and

$$Z = \frac{|V|}{|I|} e^{j(\phi_1 - \phi_2)}$$

Again it should be noted that the magnitude of Z is given by the *quotient* of the magnitudes of the constituent phasors whilst the phase is given by the *difference* of the phases of the constituent phasors.

An interesting result is obtained for the time function of Z, that is if

$$I = |I| e^{j(\omega t + \phi_2)}$$

and

$$V = |V| e^{j(\omega t + \phi_1)}$$

then

$$Z = \frac{V}{I} = \frac{|V|}{|I|} \, e^{j(\phi_1 - \phi_2)}$$

and the time domain quantity represented by Z is time invariant and constant although its constituent phasors represent time varying quantities.

Similarly if $M = VI$ then the time function of M is

$$M = |V||I| \, e^{j(\phi_1 + \phi_2) + 2\omega t}$$

that is

$$M = |V||I| \cos(2\omega t + \phi_1 + \phi_2)$$

and as M represents a quantity which varies at twice the frequency of those quantities represented by V and I it cannot be drawn as a phasor on the phasor diagram.

5.6 Frequency-domain analysis

The complex number and phasor representation of sine waves has been shown in section 5.5 to result in much easier manipulation of the variables of electrical networks. In order to make full use of these concepts, however, it is necessary to convert the electrical networks themselves into their frequency domain equivalents. This section deals with the conversion of networks into their frequency domain equivalents and the resulting analytical procedures. These are seen to be identical with those used for resistive networks except that the algebra is complex instead of real.

5.6.1 Volt–ampere equations in the frequency domain

The time-domain volt–ampere equations for the basic circuit elements have been developed in chapters 1 and 3 and they are seen to be relationships linking two time-varying quantities. The frequency-domain version of these relationships must now be developed and they are seen to be relationships between complex phasors and to be independent of time.

Resistance and conductance

The time domain volt–ampere equation is

$$v = iR$$

Thus, if

$$i = I_m \cos(\omega t + \phi)$$

then

$$v = I_m R \cos(\omega t + \phi)$$

The frequency domain equivalence is that the current is a phasor

$$I = |I| \, e^{j\phi}$$

and the voltage is

$$V = |V| \, e^{j\phi}$$

and

$$V = R|I|\,e^{j\phi}$$

Thus the relationship between the current and voltage phasors is

$$V = IR$$

which is the frequency domain version of Ohm's law. Thus the frequency domain circuit of a resistance is still a constant, real value of R ohms as shown in fig. 5.16.

Figure 5.16   Frequency-domain symbol for the resistance element

Similarly the relationship between the two phasors for a conductance **G** is

$$I = GV$$

Again it should be noted that these phasors have moduli equal to the r.m.s. values of the variables concerned, that is

$$|I| = \frac{I_m}{\sqrt{2}}$$

The phasors may have moduli equal to the amplitudes of the variables concerned; they would then be written as

$$I_m = |I_m|\,e^{j\phi} \qquad \text{etc.}$$

Inductance
The time domain volt–ampere equation is

$$v = L\,\frac{di}{dt}$$

Thus if

$$i = I_m \cos(\omega t + \phi)$$

then

$$v = -I_m L\omega \sin(\omega t + \phi)$$

or

$$v = I_m \omega L \cos(\omega t + \phi + \pi/2)$$

The phasors of the variables are

$$I = |I|\,e^{j\phi}$$

and

$$V = |I|\omega L\,e^{j(\phi + \pi/2)}$$
$$= (|I|e^{j\phi})(\omega L\,e^{j\pi/2})$$

Therefore

$$V = I(\omega L(\cos \pi/2 + j \sin \pi/2))$$

and

$$V = I(j\omega L) \tag{5.42}$$

which is the frequency domain volt–ampere equation for the inductance and which is seen to be frequency but not time dependent.

The frequency domain circuit of the inductance is shown in fig. 5.17(a) and the complex phasor diagram in fig. 5.17(b).

(a)   (b)

Figure 5.17   Frequency-domain symbol (a) and phasor diagram (b) for the inductance element

From equation (5.42)

$$|V| = |I| \omega L$$

and

$$\arg V = \arg I + \pi/2$$

(arg V means 'the angle associated with the complex number V' thus if $V = |V| e^{j\phi}$, arg $V = \phi$). Thus, in order to obtain the voltage phasor from the current phasor two operations are necessary.

(i) The modulus of the current phasor is multiplied by ωL to obtain the modulus of the voltage phasor.
(ii) The voltage phasor is 90° displaced from the current phasor in the positive direction.

Equation (5.42) may again be thought of as a frequency domain version of Ohm's law. The quantity $j\omega L$ is termed the *impedance* of the inductance and it may be seen to be measured in ohms because it relates a voltage phasor to a current phasor. Thus

$$V = IZ_L$$

and

$$Z_L = j\omega L \text{ ohms} \tag{5.43}$$

From fig. 5.17 it is seen that for a pure inductance the current always *lags* the voltage in phase by 90°.

Mutual inductance

Mutual inductance transforms to the frequency domain in the same way as self-inductance. The induced voltage leads the current by 90°. In the frequency domain the volt–ampere equations become

$$V_1 = j\omega L_1 I_1 + j\omega M I_2$$

and

$$V_2 = j\omega M I_1 + j\omega L_2 I_2$$

The effect of the mutual inductance is to add to the circuit a mutual reactance X_m or a mutual impedance Z_m, that is

$$Z_m = j X_m = j\omega M$$

The frequency domain circuit of two coils possessing mutual inductance is shown in fig. 5.18 (a) and the equivalent generator version is shown in fig. 5.18 (b).

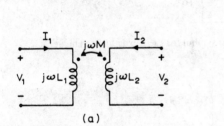 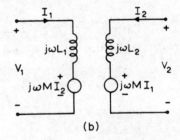

(a)   (b)

Figure 5.18   Frequency-domain symbol for mutual inductance and equivalent voltage-generator circuit

Capacitance

The time domain volt–ampere equation is

$$i = C \frac{dv}{dt}$$

thus if

$$v = V_m \cos(\omega t + \phi)$$

then

$$i = V_m \omega C \cos(\omega t + \phi + \pi/2)$$

The phasors of the variables are

$$V = |V| e^{j\phi}$$

and

$$I = |V| \omega C \, e^{j(\phi + \pi/2)}$$

Thus

$$I = (j\omega C) V \tag{5.44}$$

which is the frequency-domain volt–ampere equation for a capacitance. The impedance of the capacitance is thus

$$Z_C = \frac{1}{j\omega C} \text{ ohms} \tag{5.45}$$

or

$$Z_C = -\frac{j}{\omega C} \text{ ohms}$$

The frequency-domain circuit for a capacitance is shown in fig. 5.19 and the phasor diagram in fig. 5.20.

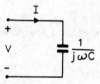

Figure 5.19   Frequency-domain symbol for the capacitance element

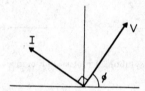

Figure 5.20   Phasor-diagram for the capacitance element

The frequency-domain representations of both capacitance and inductance are seen to be complex numbers with no real parts. With relation to phasor diagrams they are seen to be phasor operators which operate upon both the modulus and argument of a complex phasor.

5.6.2   Kirchhoff's laws in the frequency domain

The time domain version of Kirchhoff's laws were shown in chapter 1 to be

$$\sum v_n = 0 \quad \text{and} \quad \sum i_n = 0$$

Under steady-state sinusoidal conditions all the variables must have the same frequency and Kirchhoff's laws become

$$\sum V_{mn} \cos(\omega t + \phi_{nv}) = 0 \tag{5.46}$$

and

$$\sum I_{mn} \cos(\omega t + \phi_{ni}) = 0 \tag{5.47}$$

Each of the variables may be represented by a phasor and the frequency-domain version of Kirchhoff's laws becomes

$$\sum V_n = 0 \tag{5.48}$$

and

$$\sum I_n = 0 \tag{5.49}$$

Equation (5.48) states that the sum of the phasors representing the voltages existing around a loop must be zero and thus the phasors must form a closed polygon when they are added together. Alternatively, equation (5.48) states that the sum of the real parts and the sum of the imaginary parts of the complex phasors must both be zero, that is

$$\sum V_{rn} = 0 \quad \text{and} \quad \sum V_{in} = 0$$

Similar arguments apply to equation (5.49).

5.6.3 Mesh and nodal analysis

The methods of analysis discussed in chapter 2 may be used in the frequency domain but there is one important difference. The variables of the resistive networks discussed in chapter 2 were all real and ordinary algebraic techniques were used to obtain solutions; in the frequency domain, all the variables are complex numbers and hence complex algebra must be used. In addition, it is necessary to transform the time-domain circuits into the frequency-domain and it is advisable to draw a frequency-domain version of the circuit diagram.

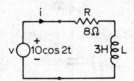

Figure 5.21   Time-domain RL circuit with sinusoidal excitation

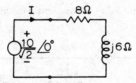

Figure 5.22   Frequency-domain equivalent of the circuit of fig. 5.21

As a simple example consider the RL circuit of fig. 5.21. The frequency domain equivalent is shown in fig. 5.22. The resistance transforms to an impedance of 8 real ohms whilst the inductance transforms to an impedance of $j\omega L$ or j 2 × 3 = j 6 'imaginary' ohms.

The total impedance of the circuit is then

$Z = 8 + j6$ ohms in the rectangular form

or

$$Z = \sqrt{(8^2 + 6^2)} \angle \tan^{-1} \tfrac{6}{8}$$

and

$$Z = 10 \angle 37° \text{ in the polar form}$$

Thus

$$I = \frac{V}{Z} = \frac{10/\sqrt{2} \angle 0°}{10 \angle 37°} = \frac{1}{\sqrt{2}} \angle - 37°$$

and

$$I = \frac{1}{\sqrt{2}} e^{j(-37°)}$$

Transforming the current back to a time function

$$i = 1 \cos(2t - 37°)$$

As an example of mesh analysis in the frequency domain, consider the circuit of fig. 5.23 which is similar to fig. 4.1 (a). The frequency domain equivalent circuit is shown in fig. 5.24.

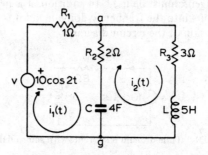

Figure 5.23   Time-domain circuit

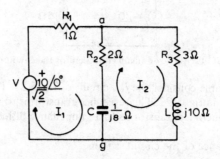

Figure 5.24   Equivalent frequency-domain circuit of the circuit of fig. 5.23

The mesh currents of

$$i_1(t) = I_{m1} \cos{(\omega t + \phi_1)}$$

and

$$i_2(t) = I_{m2} \cos{(\omega t + \phi_2)}$$

transform to the phasors I_1 and I_2 in the frequency domain such that

$$I_1 = |I_1| \, e^{j\phi_1} \qquad \text{and} \qquad |I_1| = \frac{I_{m1}}{\sqrt{2}}$$

$$I_2 = |I_2| \, e^{j\phi_2} \qquad \text{and} \qquad |I_2| = \frac{I_{m2}}{\sqrt{2}}$$

The mesh equations in the frequency domain are

$$(I_1)1 + (I_1 - I_2)2 + \frac{(I_1 - I_2)}{j8} = \frac{10}{\sqrt{2}} \angle 0°$$

and

$$(I_2)3 + (I_2)j10 + \frac{(I_2 - I_1)}{j8} + (I_2 - I_1)2 = 0$$

Rearranging gives

$$I_1\left(3 - \frac{j}{8}\right) - I_2\left(2 - \frac{j}{8}\right) = \frac{10}{\sqrt{2}} \angle 0°$$

and

$$-I_1\left(2 - \frac{j}{8}\right) + I_2\left(5 + j10 - \frac{j}{8}\right) = 0$$

A solution may therefore be found for the complex phasors I_1 and I_2.

The circuit of fig. 5.23 may also be solved by nodal analysis. Writing Kirchhoff's current law at the single independent node a gives

$$\frac{V_a - 10/\sqrt{2}}{1} + \frac{V_a}{2 - j/8} + \frac{V_a}{3 + j10} = 0$$

where V_a is the phasor of the node voltage.

Thus

$$V_a\left(\frac{1}{1} + \frac{1}{2 - j/8} + \frac{1}{3 + j10}\right) = \frac{10}{\sqrt{2}}$$

And a solution may be found for the complex phasor V_a.

Thévenin's and Norton's theorems also may be used for frequency-domain networks.

5.6.4 Impedance and admittance

In chapter 1 it was shown that a one-port resistive network could be reduced to a single equivalent resistance. Similarly, in the frequency domain, a one-port RLC network in the sinusoidal steady-state can be reduced to a single equivalent impedance. The impedance will in general be complex and its real and imaginary parts may be represented by a resistance and a capacitance or an inductance depending upon the sign of the imaginary part.

The impedance of a one-port network (also termed the 'driving-point impedance') is the ratio of the voltage phasor applied at its terminals divided by the current flowing into the terminals. Thus

$$Z = \frac{V}{I} \, \Omega \tag{5.50}$$

The impedance is generally complex and may be split into its real and imaginary parts as

$$Z = R + jX \tag{5.51}$$

where R is termed the resistance of the network in ohms and X is termed the *reactance* of the network in ohms. The reactance may be positive or negative.

The reciprocal of the impedance is

$$Y = \frac{I}{V} = \frac{1}{Z} \tag{5.53}$$

and is termed the *admittance* of the network and is measured in siemens. Again the admittance may be split into its real and imaginary parts as

$$Y = G + jB \tag{5.54}$$

where G is termed the conductance of the network in siemens and B is termed the *susceptance* of the network in siemens. It should be noted that

$$G \neq \frac{1}{R} \quad \text{and} \quad B \neq \frac{1}{X}$$

because

$$Y = \frac{1}{Z} = \frac{1}{R + jX} = \frac{R}{R^2 + X^2} - \frac{jX}{R^2 + X^2}$$

thus

$$G = \frac{R}{R^2 + X^2} \quad \text{and} \quad B = -\frac{X}{R^2 + X^2} \tag{5.55}$$

Consider again the network of fig. 5.23. The impedance of the $R_3 + L$ branch is

$$Z_3 = R_3 + j\omega L = 3 + j10$$

The impedance of the $R_2 + C$ branch is

$$Z_2 = R_3 + \frac{1}{j\omega C} = 2 - \frac{j}{8}$$

The total impedance of the two branches in parallel is

$$\frac{1}{Z_T} = \frac{1}{Z_3} + \frac{1}{Z_2}$$

and

$$\frac{1}{Z_T} = \frac{1}{3 + j10} + \frac{1}{2 - j/8}$$

and

$$Z_T = \frac{Z_2 Z_3}{Z_2 + Z_3}$$

$$= \frac{(3 + j10)(2 - j/8)}{(3 + j10) + (2 - j/8)}$$

Thus Z_T may be determined as a complex number. Similarly the total admittance of the two parallel branches is

$$Y_T = \frac{1}{Z_T} = \frac{1}{3 + j10} + \frac{1}{2 - j/8}$$

and, again, Y_T may be determined as a complex number.

5.7   Worked example

The elements of frequency domain network analysis have been discussed in section 5.6. As with any type of analysis the best way of illustrating and understanding the methods involved is to solve numerical problems with them. This section is concerned solely with the solution of several problems of this type.

5.7.1   By phasor diagram

The circuit shown in fig. 5.25 represents a generator supplying an RLC load via a transmission line which is represented by the inductance L_T and the resistance R_T. It is required to find the generator voltage and current in amplitude and phase if the load voltage, v_L, has an r.m.s. value of 240 V at a frequency of 50 Hz.

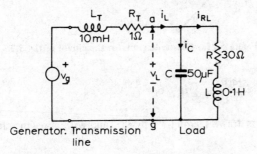

Figure 5.25   Circuit for worked example 5.7

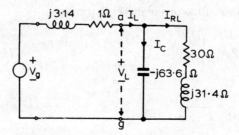

Figure 5.26   Frequency-domain equivalent of the circuit of fig. 5.25

The first step is to transform the circuit to its frequency domain equivalent which is illustrated in fig. 5.26. Thus

$$X_L = \omega L = 2\pi \times 50 \times 0.1 = 31.4 \ \Omega$$

$$X_C = \frac{1}{\omega C} = \frac{1}{2\pi \times 50 \times 50 \times 10^{-6}} = 63.7 \ \Omega$$

and

$$X_T = \omega L_T = 2\pi \times 50 \times 10 \times 10^{-3} = 3.14 \ \Omega$$

Working in the r.m.s. values of the variables throughout and plotting the phasor diagram as the analysis progresses then

$$I_{RL} = \frac{V_L}{Z_{RL}} = \frac{240}{30 + j31.4} = \frac{240}{43.5 \ \angle \ 46° \ 24'} = 5.52 \ \angle -46° \ 24'$$

The phasor diagram is shown in fig. 5.27. Setting V_L as the reference phasor then the phasor I_{RL} is constructed with a magnitude of 5.52 A lagging V_L by 46° 24'.

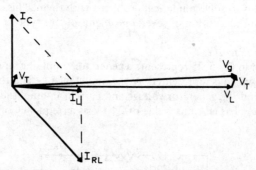

Figure 5.27   Phasor diagram for the circuit of fig. 5.25

$$I_C = \frac{V_L}{-jX_C} = \frac{240}{-j63.7} = 3.78 \ \angle \ 90°$$

The phasor I_C is drawn leading V_L by 90° and with a magnitude of 3.78 A. But

$$I_L = I_{RL} + I_C$$

therefore

$$I_L = 5.52 \angle -46° \, 24' + 3.78 \angle 90°$$
$$= 3.81 - j4.0 + j3.78$$

and

$$I_L = 3.81 - j0.22$$
$$= 3.81 \angle -3°$$

The phasor I_L is determined graphically by adding the phasors I_{RL} and I_C as shown. The voltage existing across the transmission line impedance is

$$V_T = I_L Z_T = (R_T + jX_T)(I_L)$$

Therefore

$$V_T = (1 + j3.142)(3.81 - j0.22)$$

and

$$V_T = 4.5 + j11.8 = 12.6 \angle 69°$$

By Kirchhoff's voltage law

$$V_g = V_L + V_T$$

Therefore

$$V_g = 240 + 4.5 + j11.8$$

and

$$V_g = 244.5 + j11.8$$

and

$$V_g = 244.5 \angle +3°$$

V_g is determined graphically by adding the phasor V_T to the phasor V_L as shown. In time domain form if

$$v_L = 240\sqrt{2} \cos(314t)$$

then

$$i_L = 3.81\sqrt{2} \cos(314t - 0.052)$$

and

$$v_g = 244.5\sqrt{2} \cos(314t + 0.052)$$

5.7.2 By Nodal Analysis

The circuit of fig. 5.25 and its associated problem may also be solved by nodal or mesh analysis. Writing the Kirchhoff current law equation for the **single node a** gives

$$(V_L - V_g)Y_T + V_L Y_C + V_L Y_{RL} = 0$$

Thus

$$V_g = V_L(Y_T + Y_C + Y_{RL})Z_T$$

and

$$\frac{V_g}{V_L} = 1 + Y_C Z_T + Y_{RL} Z_T$$

Here

$$Y_C = j\omega C = j0.0157 \text{ S},$$
$$Z_T = R_T + j\omega L_T = 1 + j3.14 \ \Omega$$

and

$$Y_{RL} = \frac{1}{Z_{RL}} = \frac{1}{R + jX_L} = \frac{R}{R^2 + X_L^2} - \frac{jX_L}{R^2 + X_L^2}$$

Thus

$$Y_{RL} = G - jB$$

and

$$G = \frac{30}{43.5^2} = 0.0159 \text{ S}$$

and

$$B = \frac{31.4}{(43.5^2)} = 0.0166 \text{ S}$$

Therefore

$$\frac{V_g}{V_L} = 1 + Y_C Z_T + Y_{RL} Z_T$$
$$= 1 + j0.0157(1 + j3.14) + (0.0159 - j0.0166)(1 + j3.14)$$
$$= 1 - 0.0493 + 0.0159 + 0.0521 + j(0.0157 - 0.0166 + 0.05)$$
$$= 1.0187 + j0.0491$$

Therefore

$$V_g = 240(1.0187 + j0.0491)$$

and

$$V_g = 244.3 + j11.8$$

or

$$V_g = 244.3 \angle +3°$$

5.7.3   By Thévenin Substitution

The problem associated with fig. 5.25 may also be solved by a Thévenin substitution.

Replacing the circuit to the left of and including the capacitance by its Thévenin equivalent.

Then

$$V_{Th} = V_g \frac{Z_C}{Z_T + Z_C}$$

where V_{Th} is the open-circuit voltage at the terminals ag when Z_{RL} is removed. The Thévenin equivalent impedance is the impedance of the network to the left of terminals ag when V_g is set to zero.

Thus

$$Z_{Th} = \frac{Z_C Z_T}{Z_C + Z_T}$$

When the Thévenin equivalent circuit is connected to the load Z_{RL}, the load voltage is

$$V_L = V_{Th} \times \frac{Z_{RL}}{Z_{Th} + Z_{RL}}$$

Substituting for V_{Th} gives

$$V_L = V_g \left(\frac{Z_C}{Z_T + Z_C} \right) \left(\frac{Z_{RL}}{Z_{Th} + Z_{RL}} \right)$$

Therefore

$$\frac{V_g}{V_L} = \frac{(Z_T + Z_C)(Z_{Th} + Z_{RL})}{Z_C Z_{RL}}$$

Substituting for Z_{Th} gives

$$\left(\frac{V_g}{V_L} = \frac{Z_T + Z_C}{Z_C Z_{RL}} \right) \left(Z_{RL} + \frac{Z_C Z_T}{Z_C + Z_T} \right)$$

and

$$\frac{V_g}{V_L} = \frac{1}{Z_C Z_{RL}} (Z_T Z_{RL} + Z_C Z_{RL} + Z_C Z_T)$$

Thus

$$\frac{V_g}{V_L} = 1 + \frac{Z_T}{Z_{RL}} + \frac{Z_T}{Z_C}$$

and

$$\frac{V_g}{V_L} = 1 + Z_T Y_{RL} + Z_T Y_C$$

which is the same equation which resulted from the nodal analysis of the problem.

5.8 Power in the frequency domain

The a.c. power associated with RLC networks in the time domain has been discussed in section 5.4. The use of frequency-domain methods to analyse RLC circuits has been shown to result in simpler, easier procedures and it is to be expected that the power associated with a.c. networks may also be obtained more easily by using frequency-domain methods. This section discusses the use of frequency-domain techniques to obtain the power associated with a.c. networks. The frequency-domain version of the maximum power transfer theorem is also covered.

5.8.1 Real, reactive and apparent power

A circuit containing resistive and reactive elements carrying alternating currents has associated with it voltages and currents of the form

$$v = V_m \cos \omega t$$

and

$$i = I_m \cos (\omega t - \phi)$$

and for an inductive branch the phase angle ϕ would be positive.

The instantaneous power associated with a branch of this type is

$$p = vi = V_m I_m \cos (\omega t - \phi) \cos \omega t \tag{5.56}$$

and

$$p = \frac{V_m I_m}{2} \cos \phi + \frac{V_m I_m}{2} \cos (2\omega t - \phi)$$

or

$$p = (VI \cos \phi + VI \cos \phi \cos 2\omega t) + (VI \sin \phi \sin 2\omega t) \tag{5.57}$$

The term in the first bracket of equation (5.57) relates to the real or active power. The real power is defined as

$$P = VI \cos \phi \tag{5.58}$$

The term in the second bracket of equation (5.57) has been defined as the reactive power and it has a peak value of

$$Q = VI \sin \phi \tag{5.59}$$

If ϕ is positive for an inductive circuit then Q will be positive. The reactive power is regarded as negative for a capacitive circuit.

Transferring the current and voltage variables to the frequency domain results in two r.m.s. phasors or

$$V = |V| \angle \phi_v$$

and

$$I = |I| \angle \phi_i$$

where

$$\phi_v - \phi_i = \phi$$

If the product of these two phasors is taken in order to determine the power associated with them then

$$VI = |V||I| \angle \phi_v + \phi_i \qquad \text{NOT POWER}$$

The angle obtained is $(\phi_v + \phi_i)$ and not $(\phi_v - \phi_i)$ which is the angle required for the formation of the active and reactive power equations (5.58) and (5.59) and therefore the power cannot be obtained by multiplying the current and voltage phasors. However, the conjugate phasor for I is

$$I^* = |I| \angle -\phi_i$$

and if the product of the voltage phasor and the conjugate current phasor is taken then

$$VI^* = |V||I| \angle \phi_v - \phi_i \qquad V^*I = |V||I| \angle -\phi = P - jQ \quad \text{NOT USED}$$
$$= |V||I| \angle \phi$$

Expanding gives

$$VI^* = |V||I| \cos \phi + j|V||I| \sin \phi$$

and thus

$$VI^* = P + jQ \tag{5.60}$$

Therefore, in order to determine the power associated with a branch the product of the voltage phasor and the complex conjugate of the current phasor is required.

The product $|V||I|$ is termed the *apparent power*, $|S|$, and the *complex power*

$$S = P \pm jQ.$$

Thus complex power = real power + j (reactive power). The apparent power is measured in volt–amperes; the real power is measured in watts; the reactive power is measured in volt–amperes-reactive or *vars*.

5.8.2   Power triangle

The equivalent impedance and power of a one-port network can be illustrated graphically by the use of impedance and power triangles. Similarly, the equivalent admittance and power associated with a one-port network can be illustrated by admittance and power triangles. Consider an *RLC* one-port network which, at a frequency of ω, has an equivalent impedance of

$$Z = R + jX \tag{5.61}$$

The *impedance triangle* of the network may be constructed as shown in fig. 5.28. If the r.m.s. current supplied to the network is represented by the phasor I, then multiplying equation (5.61) by I gives

$$ZI = RI + jXI$$

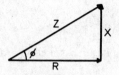

Figure 5.28   Impedance triangle of a one-port network

But ZI is the voltage at the port, that is

$$V = RI + jXI \tag{5.62}$$

RI and XI are the voltages existing on the equivalent impedance of the network as shown in Fig. 5.29.

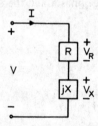

Figure 5.29   Illustration of the equivalent impedance of a one-port network

The *voltage* triangle of the network may be constructed as shown in fig. 5.30. The voltage triangle may also be derived from the phasor diagram of the equivalent network which is shown in fig. 5.31. The impedance and voltage triangles are obviously similar.

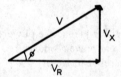

Figure 5.30   Voltage triangle of a one-port network

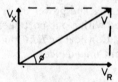

Figure 5.31   Phasor diagram of a one-port network

Multiplying equation (5.62) by I^* gives

$$VI^* = R|I|^2 + j|I|^2 X$$

But from fig. 5.28

$$R = |Z| \cos \phi$$

and

$$X = |Z| \sin \phi$$

therefore

$$VI^* = |I|^2 |Z| \cos \phi + j |I|^2 |Z| \sin \phi$$

But

$$|I||Z| = |V|$$

thus

$$VI^* = |V||I| \cos \phi + j |V||I| \sin \phi$$

and from equation (5.60)

$$VI^* = S$$
$$|V||I| \cos \phi = P$$

and

$$|V||I| \sin \phi = Q$$

Thus

$$S = P + jQ$$

and the *power* triangle of the network is obtained by multiplying the voltage triangle by $|I|$ as shown in fig. 5.32. The power, impedance and voltage triangles are all similar.

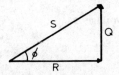

Figure 5.32   Power triangle of a one-port network

Similar admittance, current and power triangles may be obtained for a parallel circuit.

5.8.3 Worked example

Consider the circuit of fig. 5.33 which consists of a capacitance of 1 μF and a conductance of 1 mS in parallel connected to a source of 200 cos 1000t mA. It is

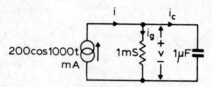

Figure 5.33   Circuit for worked example 5.8.3

required to find the apparent, real and reactive powers supplied by the source.
    The admittance of the circuit is

$$Y = G + jB$$
$$= G + j\omega C$$
$$= 10^{-3}\sqrt{2}\angle 45°$$

The frequency-domain version of the circuit is shown in fig. 5.34 and the admittance triangle is shown in fig. 5.35.

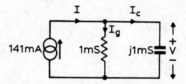

Figure 5.34   Frequency-domain equivalent of the circuit of fig. 5.33

Figure 5.35   Admittance triangle of the circuit of fig. 5.33

The r.m.s. value of the source voltage is

$$V = \frac{I}{Y}$$

where I is the r.m.s. current phasor. Thus

$$V = \frac{0.141 \angle 0°}{1.41 \times 10^{-3} \angle 45°} = 10^2 \angle -45°$$

The branch currents are

$$I_G = VG = 10^{-3} \times 10^2 \angle -45° = 0.1 \angle -45°$$

and

$$I_C = VjB = 10^2 \angle -45° \times 10^{-3} \angle 90° = 0.1 \angle +45°$$

The phasor diagram is shown in fig. 5.36 and the current triangle in fig. 5.37.

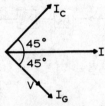

Figure 5.36 Phasor diagram of the circuit of fig. 5.33

Figure 5.37 Current triangle of the circuit of fig. 5.33

The power associated with the circuit is given by

$$VI^* = 10^2 \angle -45° \times 0.141 \angle 0°$$
$$= 14.1 \angle -45°$$

and

$$VI^* = (10 - j10)$$

Thus

$$|S| = 14.1 \text{ VA}$$
$$P = 10 \text{ W}$$
$$Q = -10 \text{ VAr.}$$

The power triangle is shown in fig. 5.38.

Figure 5.38 Power triangle of the circuit of fig. 5.33

5.8.4 *Maximum power transfer theorem*

The conditions under which maximum power could be drawn from a physical source consisting of an ideal source and an internal resistance have been discussed in chapter 2. It was shown that maximum power was obtained when the load resistance equalled the internal source resistance. When the physical source consists of an ideal source plus a complex impedance and the load is also a complex impedance similar conditions exist for the production of maximum power.

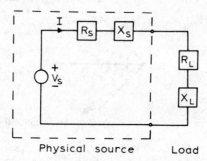

Figure 5.39   Illustration of the frequency-domain equivalent of the maximum power transfer from a voltage source

Consider the circuit of fig. 5.39 which shows the general case of a physical source which is represented in the frequency domain by a voltage source V_s and an internal source impedance $R_s + jX_s$ (X_s may be positive or negative). The load consists of a series R_L, X_L combination as shown.

Consider that both R_L and X_L may be varied in order to obtain maximum power from the source.

The current in the circuit is

$$I = \frac{V}{(R_s + R_L) + j(X_s + X_L)} \tag{5.63}$$

The power dissipated by the load resistance is the power supplied by the source, thus

$$P_L = |I|^2 R_L = \frac{|V_s|^2 R_L}{(R_s + R_L)^2 + (X_s + X_L)^2} \tag{5.64}$$

To obtain the maximum power which may be obtained by varying X_L the derivative of the power with respect to X_L is set to zero, that is

$$\frac{dP_L}{dX_L} = |V|^2 R_L \left\{ \frac{-2(X_s + X_L)}{[(R_s + R_L)^2 + (X_s + X_L)^2]^2} \right\}.$$

Thus if

$$\frac{dP_L}{dX_L} = 0$$

then

$$X_L = -X_s \qquad (5.65)$$

This result is also obtained from a consideration that maximum current occurs when the circuit is at resonance, that is when $X_L = -X_s$. Thus at resonance, or when $X_L = -X_s$,

$$P_L = \frac{|V|^2 R_L}{(R_s + R_L)^2} \qquad (5.66)$$

and the value of R_L to give maximum power is, as before,

$$R_L = R_s \qquad (5.67)$$

The conditions for maximum power are thus

$$X_L = -X_S$$

MAX POWER

and

GIVES RESONANCE

$$\underline{R_L = R_S}$$

$P_L(max) = \dfrac{V_s}{4R_s}$

ALSO BEING ADSORBED BY GENERATOR

It should be noted that these conditions are true only when both R_L and X_L may be varied. If X_L is fixed and not equal to $-X_S$ then the conditions for maximum power imposed on R_L will *not* be $R_L = R_S$. In order to determine the conditions for maximum power it is then necessary to differentiate equation (5.64) with respect to R_L and to set the differential to zero.

For a physical source which may be represented by an ideal current source in parallel with an admittance $G_S + jB_S$ feeding a load admittance $G_L + jB_L$ it may similarly be shown that the conditions for maximum power are

$$G_L = G_S$$

$P_L(max) = \dfrac{I_s}{4G_s}$

and

$$B_L = -B_S.$$

Consider now the case which is commonly encountered where R_L and X_L are not independently variable but only the modulus of the load impedance may be varied. (This case occurs when transformers are used for load matching.)

Writing

$$R_L = |Z_L| \cos \phi \quad \text{and} \quad X_L = |Z_L| \sin \phi$$

and substituting in equation (5.64) gives

$$P_L = \frac{|V|^2 |Z_L| \cos \phi}{(R_s + |Z_L| \cos \phi)^2 + (X_s + |Z_L| \sin \phi)^2}$$

To find the conditions for maximum power the derivative of the power with respect to $|Z_L|$ is set to zero.

$$\frac{dP}{d|Z_L|} = |V|^2 \left\{ \frac{\left[(\text{denominator}) \cos \phi - |Z_L| \cos \phi \left(\begin{array}{c} 2(R_s + |Z_L| \cos \phi) \cos \phi \\ + 2(X_s + |Z_L| \sin \phi) \sin \phi \end{array} \right) \right]}{(\text{denominator})^2} \right\}$$

Thus for $dP/d|Z_L| = 0$,

$$(\text{denominator}) - 2|Z_L| \{ (R_s + |Z_L| \cos \phi) \cos \phi + (X_s + |Z_L| \sin \phi) \sin \phi \} = 0$$

and

$$R_s^2 + 2R_s|Z_L| \cos \phi + |Z_L|^2 \cos^2 \phi + X_s^2 + 2X_s|Z_L| \sin \phi + |Z_L|^2 \sin^2 \phi$$
$$- 2R_s|Z_L| \cos \phi - 2|Z_L|^2 \cos^2 \phi - 2X_s|Z_L| \sin \phi - 2|Z_L|^2 \sin^2 \phi = 0$$

Therefore

$$R_s^2 + X_s^2 = |Z_L|^2$$

and

$$|Z_L| = \sqrt{(R_s^2 + X_s^2)} \tag{5.68}$$

The condition for maximum power transfer is thus that the modulus of the load impedance must equal the modulus of the source internal impedance.

Problems

5.1   In the circuit of fig. 5.40, a constant-amplitude, variable-frequency, current source supplies a parallel *GLC* circuit consisting of a 0.5 mS conductance, a 1 μF capacitance and a 1 H inductance. If the current source has a constant amplitude of 1 mA determine expressions for (a) the source voltage, and (b) the current in the inductance at some frequency ω. (c) Plot the amplitude frequency response of the source voltage and the inductance current. If the inductance current amplitude exceeds that of the source at any frequency explain why. (d) What is the resonant frequency, the bandwidth and the Q-factor of the circuit? Determine the frequencies at which the inductance current is 0.707 of its maximum possible value.

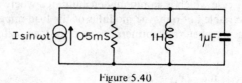

Figure 5.40

5.2   A parallel GLC circuit is supplied by a variable-frequency, constant-amplitude, alternating-current source. Show that the bandwidth of the circuits is G/C rad s^{-1} and the Q-factor is $\omega_0 C/G$. The bandwidth is defined as $(\omega_2 - \omega_1)$ where ω_2 and ω_1 are the frequencies at which the source voltage amplitude is 0.707 of its maximum possible value. Show that at the frequencies ω_1 and ω_2 the source voltage either lags or leads the source current by 45°.

5.3   In the circuit shown in fig. 5.41 an RLC circuit is connected to a constant-amplitude, variable-frequency, current source. Determine the source frequency at which the current through the inductance is a maximum and the maximum value of the inductance current in terms of the source current.

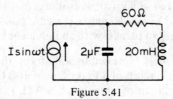

Figure 5.41

5.4   Determine the mean power, power factor, r.m.s. currents and r.m.s. voltages of the following circuits: (a) a 1 H inductance in parallel with a 0.2 S conductance connected to a source of $2 \sin 10t$ A; (b) a 1 μF capacitance in series with a 1000 Ω resistance connected to a source of $10 \cos 1000t$ V; (c) a 1 mH inductance in series with a 1 nF capacitance and a 1 MΩ resistance connected to a source of $100 \cos 1\,000\,000t$ V.

5.5   Calculate the mean and r.m.s. values of the following waveforms, each of amplitude 10 V. (a) a sine wave; (b) a triangular wave; (c) a square wave; (d) the half-wave rectified sine wave shown in fig. 5.42(a); (e) the full-wave rectified sine wave shown in fig. 5.42(b).

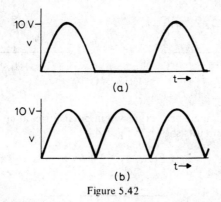

Figure 5.42

5.6   A sinusoidal voltage source of amplitude 10 V and period 1 ms is connected to a circuit consisting of a conductance of 0.1 S, an inductance of 1 mH and a capacitance of 50 μF in parallel. Draw the phasor diagram of the circuit and determine from it the source current as a function of time. Determine the source current by the use of complex algebra.

5.7   Determine the impedance and admittance expressed in both polar and rectangular forms of the following circuits at a frequency of 50 Hz.

(a) a resistance of 30 Ω in series with a capacitance of 100 μF.

(b) a resistance of 30 Ω in parallel with an inductance of 0.1 H.

(c) a resistance of 30 Ω in series with a capacitance of 100 μF and an inductance of 0.1 H.

(d) a resistance of 30 Ω in parallel with a capacitance of 100 μF and an inductance of 0.1 H.

5.8   Determine the impedance expressed in polar form, of the following circuits at a frequency of 1000 Hz.

(a) an inductance of 2 H in series with a resistance of 10 kΩ.

(b) a capacitance of 1 μF in parallel with a resistance of 100 Ω.

(c) a capacitance of 20 μF in parallel with an inductance of 2 mH.

5.9   Determine the admittance, expressed in polar form, the conductance and the susceptance of the following circuits at a frequency of 100 Hz.

(a) a parallel connected circuit of a resistance of 4 Ω, a capacitance of 100 μF and an inductance of 30 mH.

(b) a series connected circuit of a resistance of 4 Ω, a capacitance of 100 μF and an inductance of 30 mH.

5.10   Determine the steady-state source voltage as a function of time when a current source of 6 sin 2t amperes is connected

(a) to the circuit shown in fig. 5.43(a);

(b) to the circuit shown in fig. 5.43(b);

(c) to the two circuits shown in fig. 5.43 connected in series;

(d) to the two circuits shown in fig. 5.43 connected in parallel.

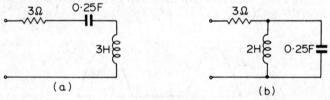

Figure 5.43

5.11   Determine the impedance, expressed in polar form, at an angular frequency of 100 rad s^{-1} of the circuits shown in fig. 5.44.

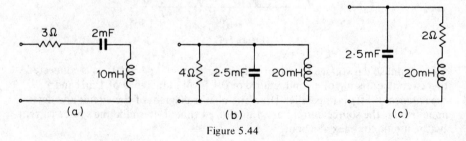

Figure 5.44

5.12   In the circuit shown in fig. 5.45, $L = 0.5$ H, $R = 10\,\Omega$ and $C = 1$ mF. (a) at what frequency is the magnitude of the impedance of the circuit zero? (b) at what frequency is the admittance of the circuit wholly conductive?

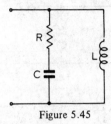

Figure 5.45

5.13   Determine the admittance, expressed in polar form, of the circuits shown in fig. 5.46 at a frequency of 100 Hz.

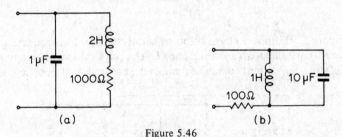

(a)   (b)

Figure 5.46

5.14   For the frequency domain circuit of fig. 5.47 determine the apparent, real and reactive powers supplied by the source.

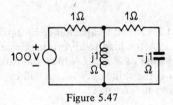

Figure 5.47

5.15   For the circuits shown in fig. 5.48 determine the apparent, real and reactive powers supplied by the sources.

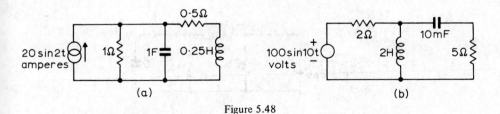

(a)   (b)

Figure 5.48

5.16   Determine the apparent, real and reactive powers supplied by the sources in the frequency domain circuits shown in fig. 5.49.

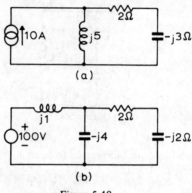

(a)

(b)

Figure 5.49

5.17   Figure 5.50 shows a physical source connected to a load consisting of a resistance R in parallel with an inductance L. The physical source is represented by an ideal alternating-current source of I amperes at an angular frequency of 10^4 rads

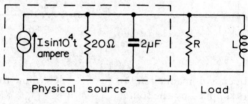

Figure 5.50

, parallel with a resistance of 20 Ω and a capacitance of 2 μF as shown. (a) what is the value of L which will cause the load to absorb maximum power if R has a value of 30 Ω? (b) what are the values of R and L which will cause the load to absorb maximum power? (c) what is the value of R which will cause the load to absorb maximum power if L has a value of 1 mH?

5.18   For the circuit of fig. 5.51 determine the values of G and C which will cause the conductance G to absorb maximum power. What is the value of the maximum power absorbed?

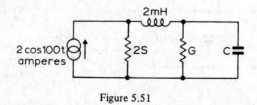

Figure 5.51

5.19   The circuit shown in fig. 5.52 represents a current generator feeding a resistive–inductive load through a transmission line. Determine the steady-state load current as a function of time and the power supplied by the generator to the transmission line.

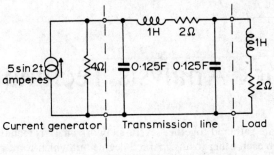

Figure 5.52

5.20   An alternating voltage generator feeding an inductive load through a transmission line is represented by the circuit shown in fig. 5.53. At the frequency at which the system operates the load has a power factor of 0.707 and the load current has an amplitude of one ampere. Determine the power absorbed by the load.

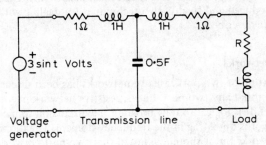

Figure 5.53

6

Network Analysis Techniques

In this chapter are gathered together several network analysis techniques which may not be related to each other to any marked degree but which form an introduction to many other analytical techniques.

The first topic covered is that relating to the behaviour of two-port networks as viewed from their terminals. The introduction given here, which includes a discussion of the ideal transformer, is necessarily brief because the subject is large. Secondly, a discussion of polyphase networks is given which may lead to further study in the fields of the generation, transmission, distribution and utilisation of electrical power. Thirdly, the important electrical measurement technique of bridge networks is introduced and finally, two techniques for dealing with particular non-linear circuits are described.

6.1 Two-port networks

The characterisation of two-port resistive networks has been discussed in chapter 2 and it was shown that any two-port, linear, resistive network may be represented by three parameters. It is logical to now broaden the discussion to include all two-port, linear RLC networks operating in the frequency domain. The discussion is limited to two-port networks but it should be noted that two-port networks are only a particular case of n-port networks.

Consider fig. 6.1 which illustrates the frequency-domain version of the general two-port network circuit diagram. The four variables at the ports are represented

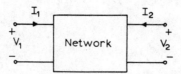

Figure 6.1   Frequency-domain equivalent of the general two-port network

by the complex phasors V_1, I_1, V_2 and I_2 and, as the network is linear, they may be related by linear equations. As discussed in chapter 2, there are six possible ways in which the four variables are related depending upon which two of the four are regarded as independent and which dependent. A brief discussion on each of the six sets follows.

6.1.1 Open-circuit impedance parameters

If the port currents are regarded as the independent variables, the port voltages are, by superposition

$$V_1 = z_{11}I_1 + z_{12}I_2 \tag{6.1}$$

and

$$V_2 = z_{21}I_1 + z_{22}I_2 \tag{6.2}$$

which are the characteristic equations of the network.

The open-circuit impedance or z parameters are defined from equations (6.1) and (6.2) and it is obvious that they have the dimensions of resistance and that they are in general complex numbers.

the open-circuit driving point impedance of port 1 is

$$z_{11} = \frac{V_1}{I_1} \qquad \text{with} \qquad I_2 = 0 \text{ (that is with port 2 on open-circuit)} \tag{6.3}$$

the open-circuit forward transfer impedance is

$$z_{21} = \frac{V_2}{I_1} \qquad \text{with} \qquad I_2 = 0 \text{ (that is with port 2 on open circuit)} \tag{6.4}$$

the open-circuit driving point impedance of port 2 is

$$z_{22} = \frac{V_2}{I_2} \qquad \text{with} \qquad I_1 = 0 \text{ (that is with port 1 on open-circuit)} \tag{6.5}$$

and the open-circuit reverse transfer impedance is

$$z_{12} = \frac{V_1}{I_2} \qquad \text{with} \qquad I_1 = 0 \text{ (that is, with port 1 on open-circuit)} \tag{6.6}$$

Each of the z parameters may be split into its resistive and reactive components, for example

$$z_{12} = r_{12} + jx_{12} \tag{6.7}$$

and for passive circuits, by the reciprocity theorem

$$z_{12} = z_{21} \tag{6.8}$$

Thus any* linear, *passive*, two-port network may be characterised by *three z* parameters.

---

* With the single exception of the *gyrator*.

Equations (6.1) and (6.2) may be quoted in matrix form as

$$\begin{bmatrix} V_1 \\ V_2 \end{bmatrix} = \begin{bmatrix} z_{11} & z_{12} \\ z_{21} & z_{22} \end{bmatrix} \begin{bmatrix} I_1 \\ I_2 \end{bmatrix} \tag{6.9}$$

where

$$[z] = \begin{bmatrix} z_{11} & z_{12} \\ z_{21} & z_{22} \end{bmatrix} \tag{6.10}$$

is termed the *open-circuit impedance matrix* of the network.

6.1.2 Short-circuit admittance parameters

If the port voltages are regarded as the independent variables, the port currents are

$$I_1 = y_{11} V_1 + y_{12} V_2 \tag{6.11}$$

and

$$I_2 = y_{21} V_1 + y_{22} V_2 \tag{6.12}$$

The short-circuit admittance parameters are defined from equations (6.11) and (6.12).

Thus the *short-circuit driving point admittance of port 1* is

$$y_{11} = \frac{I_1}{V_1} \qquad \text{with} \qquad V_2 = 0 \text{ (that is with port 2 short-circuited),} \tag{6.13}$$

the *short-circuit forward transfer admittance* is

$$y_{21} = \frac{I_2}{V_1} \qquad \text{with} \qquad V_2 = 0 \text{ (that is with port 2 short-circuited),} \tag{6.14}$$

the *short-circuit driving-point admittance of port 2* is

$$y_{22} = \frac{I_2}{V_2} \qquad \text{with} \qquad V_1 = 0 \text{ (that is with port 1 short-circuited),} \tag{6.15}$$

and the *short-circuit reverse transfer admittance* is

$$y_{12} = \frac{I_1}{V_2} \qquad \text{with} \qquad V_1 = 0 \text{ (that is with port 1 short-circuited).} \tag{6.16}$$

The matrix form of equations (6.11) and (6.12) is

$$\begin{bmatrix} I_1 \\ I_2 \end{bmatrix} = \begin{bmatrix} y_{11} & y_{12} \\ y_{21} & y_{22} \end{bmatrix} \begin{bmatrix} V_1 \\ V_2 \end{bmatrix} \tag{6.17}$$

where

$$[y] = \begin{bmatrix} y_{11} & y_{12} \\ y_{21} & y_{22} \end{bmatrix} \tag{6.18}$$

is the *short-circuit admittance matrix*.

For passive circuits, by the reciprocity theorem

$$y_{12} = y_{21}$$

and again only three y parameters are required for passive networks.

6.1.3 Hybrid parameters

The set of characteristic equations commonly used in the analysis of transistor circuitry is derived from the designation of I_1 and V_2 as the independent variables and thus

$$V_1 = h_{11}I_1 + h_{12}V_2 \tag{6.19}$$

and

$$I_2 = h_{21}I_1 + h_{22}V_2 \tag{6.20}$$

The *hybrid* or h parameters are: the *short-circuit input impedance*

$$h_{11} = \frac{V_1}{I_1} \qquad \text{with} \qquad V_2 = 0 \tag{6.21}$$

the *short-circuit forward current gain*

$$h_{21} = \frac{I_2}{I_1} \qquad \text{with} \qquad V_2 = 0 \tag{6.22}$$

the *open-circuit output admittance*

$$h_{22} = \frac{I_2}{V_2} \qquad \text{with} \qquad I_1 = 0 \tag{6.23}$$

and the *open-circuit reverse voltage gain*

$$h_{12} = \frac{V_1}{V_2} \qquad \text{with} \qquad I_1 = 0 \tag{6.24}$$

6.1.4 Inverse hybrid parameters

The dual of the hybrid parameters are the *inverse hybrid* parameters which result from V_1 and I_2 being designated the independent variables. Thus

$$I_1 = g_{11}V_1 + g_{12}I_2 \tag{6.25}$$

and

$$V_2 = g_{21} V_1 + g_{22} I_2 \tag{6.26}$$

The *inverse-hybrid* or *g* parameters are: the *open-circuit input admittance*

$$g_{11} = \frac{I_1}{V_1} \qquad \text{with} \qquad I_2 = 0 \tag{6.27}$$

the *open-circuit forward voltage gain*

$$g_{21} = \frac{V_2}{V_1} \qquad \text{with} \qquad I_2 = 0 \tag{6.28}$$

the *short-circuit output impedance*

$$g_{22} = \frac{V_2}{I_2} \qquad \text{with} \qquad V_1 = 0 \tag{6.29}$$

and the *short-circuit reverse current gain*

$$g_{12} = \frac{I_1}{I_2} \qquad \text{with} \qquad V_1 = 0 \tag{6.30}$$

6.1.5 Transmission parameters

The set of characteristic equations which are more useful for transmission line analysis and for the analysis of cascaded networks are derived from the designation of V_1 and I_1 as the independent variables or V_2 and I_2.

With V_2 and I_2 as the independent variables, the characteristic equations are

$$V_1 = a_{11} V_2 + a_{12}(-I_2) \tag{6.31}$$

and

$$I_1 = a_{21} V_2 + a_{22}(-I_2) \tag{6.32}$$

The negative sign is used in the equations because for transmission line calculations it is more convenient to consider that the current at port 2 is in the reverse direction to that shown in fig. 6.1. Thus the port current is $(-I_2)$.

The *forward transmission* parameters or *a* parameters are

$$a_{11} = \frac{V_2}{V_1} \qquad \text{with} \qquad I_2 = 0 \tag{6.33}$$

$$a_{21} = \frac{I_1}{V_2} \qquad \text{with} \qquad I_2 = 0 \tag{6.34}$$

$$a_{22} = \frac{I_1}{-I_2} \qquad \text{with} \qquad V_2 = 0 \tag{6.35}$$

and

$$a_{12} = \frac{V_1}{-I_2} \quad \text{with} \quad V_2 = 0 \tag{6.36}$$

With V_1 and I_1 as the independent variables, the characteristic equations are

$$V_2 = b_{11} V_1 + b_{12}(-I_1) \tag{6.37}$$

and

$$I_2 = b_{21} V_1 + b_{22}(-I_1) \tag{6.38}$$

The *reverse transmission* parameters are

$$b_{11} = \frac{V_2}{V_1} \quad \text{with} \quad I_1 = 0 \tag{6.39}$$

$$b_{21} = \frac{I_2}{V_1} \quad \text{with} \quad I_1 = 0 \tag{6.40}$$

$$b_{22} = \frac{I_2}{-I_1} \quad \text{with} \quad V_1 = 0 \tag{6.41}$$

and

$$b_{12} = \frac{V_2}{-I_1} \quad \text{with} \quad V_1 = 0 \tag{6.42}$$

6.1.6 Interrelation of parameters

It should be noted that any set of parameters may be derived in terms of any other set simply by manipulating the characteristic equations. As an example consider the relationship between the y parameters and the h parameters.

Equation (6.11) is

$$I_1 = y_{11} V_1 + y_{12} V_2$$

Dividing by y_{11} gives

$$V_1 = \frac{I_1}{y_{11}} - V_2 \frac{y_{12}}{y_{11}}$$

Thus from equation (6.19)

$$h_{11} = \frac{1}{y_{11}} \quad \text{and} \quad h_{12} = -\frac{y_{12}}{y_{11}}$$

Similarly from equations (6.12) and (6.20)

$$h_{21} = \frac{y_{21}}{y_{11}} \quad \text{and} \quad h_{22} = \frac{y_{11}y_{22} - y_{12}y_{21}}{y_{11}}$$

For *passive* networks it has been shown that

$$z_{12} = z_{21}$$

and

$$y_{12} = y_{21}$$

These two relationships may be shown to result in the additional identities for passive networks of

$$g_{12} = -g_{21}, h_{12} = -h_{21} \text{ (see above)} \tag{6.43}$$

and

$$(a_{11}a_{22} - a_{12}a_{21}) = (b_{11}b_{12} - b_{12}b_{21}) = 1 \tag{6.44}$$

The latter identity results in simplifications in the *a* and *b* parameters and they may be expressed in terms of the A, B, C, D parameters as

$$a_{11} = b_{22} = A$$
$$a_{12} = b_{12} = B$$
$$a_{21} = b_{21} = C$$
$$a_{22} = b_{11} = D \tag{6.45}$$

The transmission equations are then, in the matrix form,

$$\begin{bmatrix} V_1 \\ I_1 \end{bmatrix} = \begin{bmatrix} A & B \\ C & D \end{bmatrix} \begin{bmatrix} V_2 \\ -I_2 \end{bmatrix} \tag{6.46}$$

and

$$\begin{bmatrix} V_2 \\ I_2 \end{bmatrix} = \begin{bmatrix} D & B \\ C & A \end{bmatrix} \begin{bmatrix} V_1 \\ -I_1 \end{bmatrix} \tag{6.47}$$

It should also be noted that from equation (6.44)

$$AD - BC = 1 \tag{6.48}$$

The four *ABCD* parameters are thus not independent and, again, three parameters are sufficient to represent passive networks.

6.1.7 Equivalent T and Π networks

It was shown in chapter 2 that any two-port, linear, passive, resistive network could be replaced by three resistances connected in the Π or T configuration. Similarly any two-port, linear, passive network may be replaced by three impedances connected in a T configuration or three admittances connected in the Π configuration.

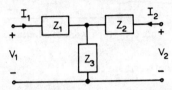

Figure 6.2 T-network of impedances

Consider the circuit shown in fig. 6.2. The z parameters of the circuit are

$$z_{11} = \frac{V_1}{I_1}$$

with port 2 on open-circuit. Hence

$$z_{11} = Z_1 + Z_3.$$

Since $I_2 = 0$, there is no potential difference across Z_2 and hence

$$z_{21} = \frac{V_2}{I_1} = Z_3$$

Similarly

$$z_{22} = Z_2 + Z_3 \qquad \text{and} \qquad z_{12} = Z_3$$

The tree elements of the T equivalent circuit are then

$$Z_3 = z_{12} = z_{21}$$
$$Z_1 = z_{11} - z_{12}$$

and

$$Z_2 = z_{22} - z_{12}$$

(6.49)

Thus any linear, passive, two-port network may be represented by the equivalent T network shown in fig. 6.3.

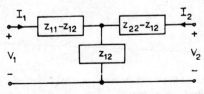

Figure 6.3 Equivalent T circuit

Consider now the Π network shown in fig. 6.4.

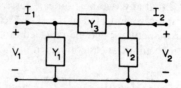

Figure 6.4   Π-network of admittances

The y parameters of the network are

$$y_{11} = \frac{I_1}{V_1}$$

with port 2 short-circuited. Hence

$$y_{11} = Y_1 + Y_3$$

With port 2 short-circuited

$$I_2 = -\frac{V_1}{Y_3}$$

Hence

$$y_{21} = \frac{I_2}{V_1} = -Y_3$$

Similarly

$$y_{22} = Y_2 + Y_3$$

and

$$y_{12} = -Y_3$$

The three elements of the Π equivalent network are then

$$Y_1 = y_{11} + y_{12}$$
$$Y_2 = y_{22} + y_{12}$$

(6.50)

and

$$Y_3 = -y_{12} = -y_{21}$$

Thus any linear, passive, two-port network may be represented by the Π equivalent circuit shown in fig. 6.5.

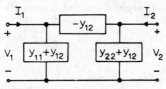

Figure 6.5   Equivalent Π circuit

6.2 Ideal transformer

One of the simplest and most commonly used two-port networks or devices is the transformer. The simplest type of transformer consists of two coils coupled magnetically such that some of the magnetic field produced by one coil links with the other and vice versa. In this way, electrical energy may be transferred from one coil to the other and this is the principal function of the transformer.

The ideal transformer possesses perfect coupling; that is, all the magnetic field produced by one coil links with the other. As a circuit element, therefore, the ideal transformer neither dissipates nor stores energy, but merely transfers it from one circuit to another. The transformer is thus the 'gearbox' of electric circuits in that it transforms electrical energy at one potential into electrical energy at some other potential.

6.2.1 Volt–ampere equations

The two coils of the simple transformer may be separated by air as in fig. 3.8 but in order to increase the coupling between the coils they are usually wound upon a

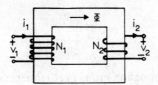

Figure 6.6   Simple iron-cored transformer

common magnetic core as shown in fig. 6.6. The input coil or *primary* winding is a coil of N_1 turns as shown. The output coil or *secondary* winding is a coil of N_2 turns as shown. The ratio of N_2 to N_1 is the *turns ratio n.* Thus

$$n = \frac{N_2}{N_1} \tag{6.51}$$

Consider that the primary winding is connected to a voltage source v_1, the source will then supply a current of i_1 to the primary. The current flowing in the primary creates a magnetic field in the permeable core and the magnetic flux created is ϕ. The volt–ampere equation of the primary circuit is then

$$v_1 = R_1 i_1 + N_1 \frac{\mathrm{d}\phi}{\mathrm{d}t} \tag{6.52}$$

The magnetic flux also links completely with the secondary winding and the voltage induced in the secondary winding is

$$v_2 = N_2 \frac{d\phi}{dt} \tag{6.53}$$

For an ideal transformer the windings are resistanceless, therefore, $R_1 = 0$. Thus

$$v_1 = N_1 \frac{d\phi}{dt}$$

and therefore

$$\frac{v_2}{v_1} = \frac{N_2}{N_1} = n \tag{6.54}$$

which is the voltage transformation ratio.

The energy stored in an ideal transformer is zero and therefore the instantaneous input power must always equal the instantaneous output power. Therefore

$$v_1 i_1 = v_2 i_2$$

and thus

$$i_2 = \frac{v_1}{v_2} i_1$$

or

$$i_2 = i_1 \frac{1}{n} \tag{6.55}$$

which is the current transformation ratio. The frequency-domain version of the ideal transformer volt–ampere equations are

$$V_2 = nV_1 \tag{6.56}$$

and

$$I_2 = \frac{1}{n} I_1 \tag{6.57}$$

The frequency-domain symbol for a transformer is shown in fig. 6.7.

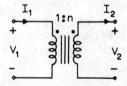

Figure 6.7   Frequency-domain symbol for an ideal transformer

In terms of the *ABCD* parameters of section 6.1.6, it is seen that

$$a_{11} = b_{22} = A = \frac{1}{n}$$

$$a_{22} = b_{11} = D = n$$

$$a_{12} = b_{12} = a_{21} = b_{21} = B = C = 0 \tag{6.58}$$

Care should be taken in the application of the two-port parameters to the ideal transformer because the notation usually adopted for the ideal transformer is that shown in fig. 6.7 where the direction of I_2 is the reverse of that of the general two-port network shown in fig. 6.1.

6.2.2 Impedance transformation

Consider the frequency domain circuit of fig. 6.8 in which an impedance Z is connected to the secondary of the transformer and a source V_1 is connected to the primary.

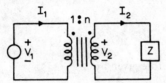

Figure 6.8   Transformer with an impedance load

The volt–ampere equation of the secondary circuit is

$$V_2 = I_2 Z_2$$

but

$$V_2 = n V_1 \qquad \text{and} \qquad I_2 = \frac{1}{n} I_1$$

Thus

$$n V_1 = \frac{I_1}{n} Z_2$$

and

$$\frac{V_1}{I_1} = \frac{1}{n^2} Z_2 \tag{6.59}$$

The effective impedance presented to the source is

$$Z_1 = \frac{V_1}{I_1}$$

thus

$$Z_1 = \frac{1}{n^2} Z_2 \tag{6.60}$$

The transformer thus possesses the property of being able to change the effective impedance presented to a source. This property of the transformer is utilised a great deal in electronic and communication circuits.

6.2.3 Voltage and magnetic flux waveforms
The fundamental equations of the ideal transformer are

$$v_1 = N_1 \frac{d\phi}{dt}$$

$$v_2 = N_2 \frac{d\phi}{dt}$$

and

$$i_1 = ni_2$$

The magnetic flux is therefore given by

$$\phi = \frac{1}{N_1} \int_{-\infty}^{t} v_1 \, dt$$

If v_1 is a steady d.c. quantity this implies that the magnetic flux will increase indefinitely and without limit. Obviously in practical transformers this cannot happen and due to the saturation of the permeable core material the flux reaches a maximum value after which it cannot change. There is then no induced voltage in the primary winding to oppose the applied voltage and very high currents will flow into the transformer. A transformer must, therefore, operate with an alternating voltage having a mean value of zero and this is frequently, although not always, a sine wave.

If the voltage v_1 is a sine wave then so will the flux vary sinusoidally with time, but it will lag the voltage by 90°, that is if

$$v_1 = V_{m1} \cos \omega t$$

then

$$\phi = \frac{1}{N_1 \omega} \sin \omega t$$

and

$$v_2 = \frac{N_2}{N_1} V_{m1} \cos \omega t$$

If the voltage applied to the secondary is a square-wave then the flux-time variation is a triangular wave as shown in fig. 6.9.

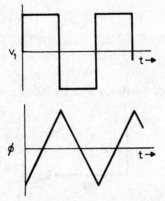

Figure 6.9 Transformer voltage and flux waveforms

6.2.4 Phasor diagrams

No-load
Consider that the ideal transformer of fig. 6.7 is operating with its secondary on open-circuit, that is, no load is connected to the secondary. If

$$\phi = \Phi_m \cos \omega t$$

then

$$\phi = \text{Re}[\Phi_m e^{j\omega t}]$$

and the flux may be represented by the phasor Φ_m as shown in fig. 6.10(a), where

$$\Phi_m = |\Phi_m| \angle 0$$

The primary voltage is then

$$v_1 = N_1 \frac{d\phi}{dt}$$

and

$$v_1 = \text{Re}[jN_1\omega\Phi_m e^{j\omega t}]$$

or

$$v_1 = \text{Re}[V_{m1} e^{j\omega t}]$$

where

$$V_{m1} = jN_1\omega\Phi_m$$

Thus the primary voltage phasor is

$$V_{m1} = |V_{m1}| \angle 90°$$

or

$$V_{m1} = |N_1 \omega \Phi_m| \angle 90°$$

and the voltage phasor leads the flux phasor by 90° as shown in fig. 6.10(a).

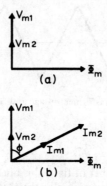

Figure 6.10   Transformer phasor diagrams: (a) no-load; (b) on-load

Similarly the secondary voltage phasor is

$$V_{m2} = |V_{m2}| \angle 90°$$

or

$$V_{m2} = |N_2 \omega \Phi_m| \angle 90°$$

as shown in fig. 6.10 (a).

On load

Consider that the ideal transformer has an impedance of Z connected to its secondary as shown in fig. 6.8. Thus if

$$Z = |Z| \angle \phi$$

then

$$I_{m2} = \frac{V_{m2}}{Z} = \frac{|V_{m2}| \angle 90°}{|Z| \angle \phi}$$

and the secondary current phasor is

$$I_{m2} = |I_{m2}| \angle 90° - \phi$$

or

$$I_{m2} = \frac{|V_{m2}|}{|Z|} \angle\ 90° - \phi$$

The secondary current phasor is shown in the on-load phasor diagram of fig. 6.10(b).
The primary current is given by

$$I_{m1} = \frac{N_2}{N_1} I_{m2} = n \frac{V_{m2}}{Z}$$

and the primary current phasor is

$$I_{m1} = |I_{m1}| \angle\ 90° - \phi$$

or

$$I_{m1} = |nI_{m2}| \angle\ 90° - \phi$$

or

$$I_{m1} = \frac{|nV_{m2}|}{|Z|} \angle\ 90° - \phi$$

and the primary current phasor is as shown in fig. 6.10(b).

6.2.5 Worked example
Consider the frequency-domain circuit of fig. 6.11. It is required to find the
magnitudes and phases of the r.m.s. current and the load voltage phasors.

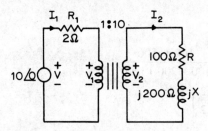

Figure 6.11   Equivalent frequency-domain circuit of transformer with load impedance

Writing the Kirchhoff voltage law equations for the two meshes gives

$$I_1 R_1 + V_1 - V = 0$$

and

$$I_2 R + jI_2 X - V_2 = 0$$

The constraint equations are

$$V_2 = nV_1$$

and

$$I_2 = \frac{I_1}{n}$$

Thus

$$V_2 = I_2(R + jX)$$

$$= \frac{I_1}{n}(R + jX)$$

$$= \frac{(V - V_1)}{nR_1}(R + jX)$$

$$= \frac{(V - V_2/n)}{nR_1}(R + jX)$$

Therefore

$$V_2 = \frac{V}{nR_1}(R + jX)\frac{1}{(1 + 1/n^2R_1)(R + jX)}$$

and

$$V_2 = Vn\left(\frac{R + jX}{R + n^2R_1 + jX}\right)$$

Thus

$$V_2 = 10 \times 10\left(\frac{100 + j200}{100 + 200 + j200}\right)$$

$$= 100\left(\frac{1 + j2}{3 + j2}\right)$$

and

$$V_2 = \frac{100}{13}(7 + j4)$$

or

$$V_2 = \frac{100}{13}\sqrt{65}\angle \tan^{-1}\tfrac{4}{7}$$

Thus

$$V_2 = 62 \angle 30°$$

Therefore

$$V_1 = 6.2 \angle 30°$$

The secondary current is given by

$$I_2 = \frac{V_2}{Z_2}$$

But

$$Z_2 = 100 + j200 = 224 \angle 64°$$

Thus

$$I_2 = \frac{62 \angle 30°}{224 \angle 64°} = 0.277 \angle -34°$$

The primary current is given by

$$I_1 = nI_2 = 10I_2$$

Thus

$$I_1 = 2.77 \angle -34°$$

The phasor diagram is shown in fig. 6.12.

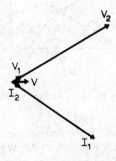

Figure 6.12   Phasor diagram for the circuit of fig. 6.11

As a check on the answers

$$V = I_1R_1 + V_1$$

Thus

$$V = 6.2 \angle 30° + (2 \times 2.77 \angle - 34°)$$
$$= 5.38 + j3.1 + 4.6 - j3.1$$

Therefore

$$V = 10 + j0$$

6.3 Bridge networks

A particular type of two-port network frequently encountered in the field of electrical measurements is the bridge network. The general bridge network consists of four impedances, a source and a detector connected as shown in fig. 6.13. The two circuits shown in fig. 6.13 are the two ways of illustrating the bridge network;

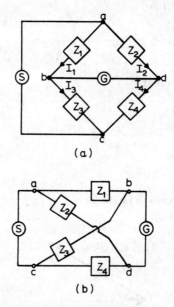

(a)

(b)

Figure 6.13   A.c. bridge circuits

they are, of course, the same circuit. If the four impedances are all resistances, the source is a d.c. one and the detector a galvanometer then the circuit is the Wheatstone bridge which is usually used for measuring unknown resistances. For the measurement of capacitance and inductance an a.c. source is used and the four impedances may all be capacitive or inductive depending upon the bridge being used.

At balance conditions on an a.c. bridge, the four impedances are so adjusted that a null reading is obtained on the detector which implies that no current is passing through the detector and hence no potential exists across it. Representing the variables by phasors and writing Kirchhoff's voltage law around the meshes give

for mesh abd $\qquad I_2 Z_2 - I_1 Z_1 = 0$

for mesh bdc $\qquad I_4 Z_4 - I_3 Z_3 = 0$

Kirchhoff's current law applied at nodes b and d gives

for node b $\qquad I_1 - I_3 = 0$

for node d $\qquad I_2 - I_4 = 0$

Thus $I_1 = I_3$ and $I_2 = I_4$ and substituting in the voltage equations gives the general balance conditions of

$$\frac{Z_1}{Z_3} = \frac{Z_2}{Z_4} \qquad (6.61)$$

In terms of the moduli and arguments of the impedances

$$\frac{|Z_1|}{|Z_2|} = \frac{|Z_3|}{|Z_4|} \qquad (6.62)$$

and

$$(\phi_1 - \phi_2) = (\phi_3 - \phi_4) \qquad (6.63)$$

Both of these conditions must be satisfied for the bridge to balance.

6.3.1 Wheatstone bridge

Consider that the source of the circuit of fig. 6.13 is a d.c. one and the impedances are all resistances then the conditions for balance are

$$R_1 = R_3 \frac{R_2}{R_4} \qquad (6.64)$$

Thus if R_1 is an unknown resistance and R_3 is a variable resistance the circuit, which is known as a Wheatstone bridge circuit, may be used to measure the unknown resistance.

6.3.2 Maxwell bridge

The Maxwell bridge for comparing or measuring capacitance and inductance usually has the impedances Z_1 and Z_4 as resistances R_1 and R_4, the impedance Z_2 as, say, an unknown series inductance/resistance circuit and the impedance Z_3 as a variable parallel capacitance/conductance circuit. Thus

$$Z_2 = R_2 + j\omega L_2$$

and

$$\frac{1}{Z_3} = G_3 + j\omega C_3$$

Thus from the general balance conditions given in equation (6.61)

$$R_1(G_3 + j\omega C_3) = \frac{(R_2 + j\omega L_2)}{R_4}$$

Thus

$$R_2 = R_1 R_4 G$$

and

$$L_2 = R_1 R_4 C \tag{6.65}$$

and the two unknowns may be determined.

It should be noted that these conditions are independent of source voltage, current or frequency.

6.4 Polyphase circuits

The a.c. circuits discussed previously have consisted solely of single-phase circuits, that is, single self-contained networks operating at a fixed frequency. In the fields of the generation, transmission, distribution and utilisation of electrical power, however, it is necessary for reasons of economics, convenience and performance to use networks consisting of several similar parallel a.c. phases coupled together to form a polyphase system. The consideration of just one aspect of polyphase systems, namely the power, will show why this is so. In a single-phase system the power has been shown to oscillate at twice the system frequency; in a balanced polyphase system the power is constant and time invariant. Thus, for instance, a single-phase motor cannot produce a constant, non-pulsating torque, whereas a polyphase motor can.

It is possible to construct polyphase systems consisting of any number of phases but the two systems most widely used are the three-phase system for electrical power systems and the so-called two-phase system which is used widely in a.c. control systems. Pure two-phase systems do not exist and the system which is widely known as the 'two-phase system' is actually one-half of a four-phase system. The discussion here will be limited to three-phase balanced circuits but the arguments and methods of analysis can obviously be applied to any polyphase circuit.

6.4.1 Balanced three-phase voltages
Consider the circuit shown in fig. 6.14 which shows a balanced three-phase, *star-connected* voltage source.

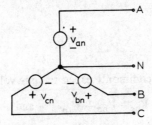

Figure 6.14 Balanced, three-phase, star-connected voltage source

The three-phase source consists of three single-phase voltage sources of the same frequency and voltage amplitude but of different time phase. The three source voltages are

$$
\left.
\begin{aligned}
v_{an} &= V_m \cos \omega t \\
v_{bn} &= V_m \cos\left(\omega t - \frac{2\pi}{3} \right) \\
v_{cn} &= V_m \cos\left(\omega t - \frac{4\pi}{3} \right)
\end{aligned}
\right\}
\tag{6.66}
$$

Thus the three source voltages are separated in time-phase by $2\pi/3$ radians. The phasor diagram of the source voltages is shown in fig. 6.15.

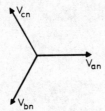

Figure 6.15 Phasor diagram for the source of fig. 6.14

The terminals A, B and C of the three-phase source are called the *line* terminals and the terminal N which is connected to the common or *star* point of the sources is termed the *neutral* terminal.

Thus the *line-to-neutral* or *phase* voltages are in phasor form,

$$
\left.
\begin{aligned}
V_{an} &= V_{ph}\, e^{j0} \\
V_{bn} &= V_{ph}\, e^{-j(2\pi/3)} \\
\text{and} \\
V_{cn} &= V_{ph}\, e^{-j(4\pi/3)}
\end{aligned}
\right\}
\tag{6.67}
$$

where

$$V_{ph} = \frac{V_m}{\sqrt{2}}$$

The *line-to-line* voltages, commonly called the *line* voltages, are

$$V_{ab} = V_{an} - V_{bn}, \qquad V_{bc} = V_{bn} - V_{cn} \qquad \text{and} \qquad V_{ca} = V_{cn} - V_{an}$$

Thus

$$\begin{aligned}
V_{ab} &= V_{ph}\, e^{j0} - V_{ph}\, e^{-j(2\pi/3)} \\
&= V_{ph}[1 - (-\tfrac{1}{2} - j\tfrac{3}{2})] \\
&= V_{ph}(\tfrac{3}{2} + j\tfrac{3}{2})
\end{aligned}$$

Let

$$V_{ab} = V_{line}\, e^{j\theta}$$

Thus

$$V_{line} \cos\theta = V_{ph}\tfrac{3}{2}$$

and

$$V_{line} \sin\theta = V_{ph}\tfrac{3}{2}$$

Solving for V_{line} and θ gives

$$V_{line} = \sqrt{3}\,V_{ph}$$

and

$$\theta = \frac{\pi}{6}$$

Thus

$$V_{ab} = \sqrt{3}\,V_{ph}\, e^{j(\pi/6)}$$

Similar calculations for V_{bc} and V_{ca} show that the phasors for the line voltages are

$$\left.\begin{aligned}
V_{ab} &= \sqrt{3}\,V_{ph}\, e^{j(\pi/6)} \\
V_{bc} &= \sqrt{3}\,V_{ph}\, e^{-j(\pi/2)} \\[6pt]
V_{ca} &= \sqrt{3}\,V_{ph}\, e^{-j(7\pi/6)}
\end{aligned}\right\} \qquad (6.68)$$

and

Thus the magnitudes of the line voltages are $\sqrt{3}$ the magnitudes of the phase voltages and the line voltages are phase *advanced* on the phase voltages by $\pi/6$ radians as shown in fig. 6.16.

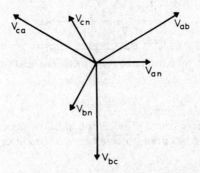

Figure 6.16   Relationship between line and phase voltage-phasors

A similar result can be obtained by subtracting the phasors graphically as shown in fig. 6.17.

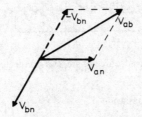

Figure 6.17   Illustration of phasor subtraction

The time-domain line voltages are then

$$v_{ab} = \sqrt{3}V_m \cos\left(\omega t + \frac{\pi}{6}\right)$$

$$v_{bc} = \sqrt{3}V_m \cos\left(\omega t - \frac{\pi}{2}\right) \tag{6.69}$$

and

$$v_{ca} = \sqrt{3}V_m \cos\left(\omega t - \frac{7\pi}{6}\right)$$

The three single-phase sources may also be connected in the balanced, three-phase, *delta-connected* system shown in fig. 6.18.

It is obvious that for the delta-connected system the phase voltages are equal to the line voltages.

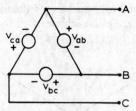

Figure 6.18   Balanced, three-phase, delta-connected voltage source

6.4.2 Balanced three-phase currents

Consider that the balanced, three-phase, star-connected impedance shown in fig. 6.19 is connected to the balanced, three-phase voltage source shown in fig. 6.14.

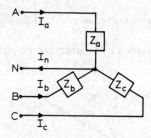

Figure 6.19   Balanced, three-phase, star-connected impedance

In a balanced, three-phase impedance

$$Z_a = Z_b = Z_c = |Z| e^{j\phi} \qquad (6.70)$$

and the three-phase currents are then

$$I_a = \frac{V_{an}}{Z_a}, \qquad I_b = \frac{V_{bn}}{Z_b} \qquad \text{and} \qquad I_c = \frac{V_{cn}}{Z_c}$$

The phase currents are thus

$$I_a = \frac{V_{ph}}{|Z|} e^{j(0-\phi)} = I_{ph} e^{j(-\phi)}$$

$$I_b = \frac{V_{ph}}{|Z|} e^{j[(-2\pi/3)-\phi]} = I_{ph} e^{j[(-2\pi/3)-\phi]}$$

and

$$I_c = \frac{V_{ph}}{|Z|} e^{j[(-4\pi/3)-\phi]} = I_{ph} e^{j[(-4\pi/3)-\phi]}$$

$$(6.71)$$

A typical phasor diagram for a resistive–inductive impedance is shown in fig. 6.20.

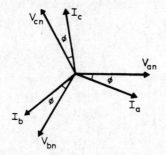

Figure 6.20   Typical balanced, three-phase, phasor diagram

For the star-connected impedance shown it is obvious that the line currents are equal to the phase currents.

The current in the neutral line is given by Kirchhoff's current law as

$$I_n = I_a + I_b + I_c \tag{6.72}$$

Substituting for I_a, I_b and I_c from equation (6.71) gives

$$I_n = 0 \tag{6.73}$$

This result may also be obtained by adding the three phasors graphically.

Thus, for a balanced, three-phase system the neutral current is *always* zero and the neutral line may be *omitted*. This explains one of the economic advantages of using polyphase systems, that is, only three wires are needed to carry the power for three phases instead of the six that would be needed if the phases were separated.

Consider now that the balanced, delta-connected, three-phase impedance shown in fig. 6.21 is connected to the delta-connected source shown in fig. 6.18.

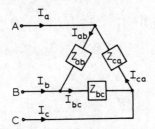

Figure 6.21   Balanced, three-phase, delta-connected impedance

It is obvious that the phase currents in the delta-connected system are not equal to the line currents.

The phase currents are

$$I_{ab} = \frac{V_{ab}}{Z_{ab}}, \quad I_{bc} = \frac{V_{bc}}{Z_{bc}} \quad \text{and} \quad I_{ca} = \frac{V_{ca}}{Z_{ca}}$$

The line currents are from Kirchhoff's current law

$$\left.\begin{array}{l} I_a = I_{ab} - I_{ca} \\ I_b = I_{bc} - I_{ab} \\ I_c = I_{ca} - I_{bc} \end{array}\right\}$$

and   (6.74)

Consider the line current I_a. Let

$$\left.\begin{array}{l} V_{ab} = V_{line}\ e^{j0} \\ V_{bc} = V_{line}\ e^{-j(2/3)} \\ V_{ca} = V_{line}\ e^{-j(4/3)} \end{array}\right\}$$ (6.75)

and

$$Z_{ab} = Z_{bc} = Z_{ca} = |Z|\ e^{j\phi}$$ (6.76)

then

$$I_{ab} = \frac{V_{ab}}{Z_{ab}} = \frac{V_{line}}{|Z|}\ e^{j(-\phi)} = I_{ph}\ e^{-j\phi}$$

and

$$I_{ca} = \frac{V_{ca}}{Z_{ca}} = V_{line}\ e^{j[(-4\pi/3)-\phi]} = I_{ph}\ e^{-j[(4\pi/3)+\phi]}$$

Thus

$$I_a = I_{ph}\ \{e^{-j\phi} - e^{-j[(4\pi/3)+\phi]}\}$$

and

$$I_a = \sqrt{3}\ I_{ph}\ e^{j[(-\pi/6)-\phi]}$$

from similar reasoning to that used to obtain the relationships between phase and line voltages for the star-connected case. This result may also be obtained graphically as shown in fig. 6.22.

The line currents are thus

$$\left.\begin{array}{l} I_a = \sqrt{3}\ I_{ph}\ e^{-j[\phi+(\pi/6)]} \\ I_b = \sqrt{3}\ I_{ph}\ e^{-j[\phi+(5\pi/6)]} \\ I_c = \sqrt{3}\ I_{ph}\ e^{-j[\phi+(3\pi/2)]} \end{array}\right\}$$ (6.77)

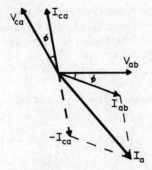

Figure 6.22   Relationship between line and phase current-phasors

Thus, for the delta-connected system, the magnitudes of the line currents are $\sqrt{3}$ times the magnitudes of the phase currents and the line currents are phase *retarded* on the phase currents by $\pi/6$ radians.

6.4.3 Three-phase power

The real power associated with each phase of a three-phase system is

$$P_{\text{ph}} = V_{\text{ph}}I_{\text{ph}} \cos \phi$$

and the total power is thus

$$P = 3P_{\text{ph}} = 3V_{\text{ph}}I_{\text{ph}} \cos \phi \tag{6.78}$$

In terms of line quantities, for the star-connected system

$$I_{\text{line}} = I_{\text{ph}}$$

and

$$V_{\text{line}} = \sqrt{3}V_{\text{ph}}$$

and thus

$$P_{\text{Y}} = \sqrt{3}V_{\text{line}}I_{\text{line}} \cos \phi \tag{6.79}$$

For the delta-connected system

$$V_{\text{line}} = V_{\text{ph}}$$

and

$$I_{\text{line}} = \sqrt{3}I_{\text{ph}}$$

and thus

$$P_{\Delta} = \sqrt{3}V_{\text{line}}I_{\text{line}} \cos \phi \tag{6.80}$$

The same power expression therefore holds for both star and delta systems.

An interesting result is obtained for the instantaneous power. Consider a star-connected, balanced system. The instantaneous power is

$$p = v_{an}i_a + v_{bn}i_b + v_{cn}i_c$$

$$= V_mI_m \cos \omega t \cos (\omega t + \phi) + V_mI_m \cos \left(\omega t - \frac{2\pi}{3} \right)$$

$$\times \cos \left(\omega t - \frac{2\pi}{3} + \phi \right) + V_mI_m \cos \left(\omega t - \frac{4\pi}{3} \right) \cos \left(\omega t - \frac{4\pi}{3} + \phi \right)$$

thus

$$p = \frac{V_mI_m}{2} \left\{ \cos (2\omega t + \phi) + \cos \phi + \cos \left(2\omega t - \frac{4\pi}{3} + \phi \right) \right.$$

$$\left. + \cos \phi + \cos \left(2\omega t - \frac{8\pi}{3} + \phi \right) + \cos \phi \right\}$$

and

$$p = \frac{V_mI_m}{2} 3 \cos \phi = 3VI \cos \phi.$$

A similar result is obtained for the delta-connected system and thus for a balanced, three-phase system, the power does not vary with time. This is a further reason for the use of·polyphase systems.

6.5 Non-linear circuits—load line and linear approximation

The circuits, networks and circuit elements considered in the previous chapters have all been linear and the methods by which they have been analysed may be used only for linear systems. The real world, however, is very seldom linear and the great majority of real circuit elements and devices are non-linear. Exact analysis of circuits containing non-linear elements is extremely difficult, if not impossible, and many different techniques exist to approximate the effects of non-linearities and to predict the behaviour of real devices within acceptable limits. These techniques are approximations, however, and in some cases whether or not a solution is obtained for a problem depends upon which approximation has been chosen. Sometimes non-linearities can be neglected and a linear approximation yields sufficiently accurate results.

Non-linearity is not always a nuisance and it may be deliberately designed into a system in order to, say, prevent the system from producing too large a response and thereby damaging itself. In such cases it is of the utmost importance to determine which type of non-linearity is best suited for the job.

This section deals with some of the simplest ways of dealing with non-linearities.

6.5.1 Non-linear elements

The following are typical of the non-linear elements which occur frequently in practical circuits.

Non-linear resistors

A resistor which has a potential across it which is not proportional to the current flowing through it is non-linear. Most physical resistors exhibit the property of increasing resistance with current and they possess a voltage/current relationship similar to that shown in fig. 6.23.

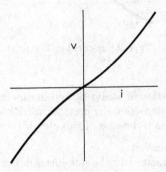

Figure 6.23   Typical non-linear resistor voltage–current characteristic

Semi-conductor diode

An ideal diode is a device which has a zero resistance to current passing through it in one direction but infinite resistance to currents attempting to pass in the other. It is therefore not a bilateral element. Physical diodes attempt to fulfil this requirement and they possess characteristics similar to that shown in fig. 6.24.

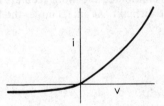

Figure 6.24   Typical semi-conductor diode characteristic

Iron-cored inductor

The inductors discussed previously have consisted of coils separated by air or a vacuum. In many requirements for inductors, however, there is a need for much higher inductance than can be obtained with air-cored coils. Highly permeable material such as iron is therefore placed around the coils which tends to increase the magnetic fields produced and hence the inductance. Most highly-permeable materials used in such iron-cored inductors have non-linear B–H characteristics and the inductors have voltage–current characteristics similar to that shown in fig. 6.25. This is an example of the classical 'saturation' non-linearity which is frequently encountered in all branches of engineering.

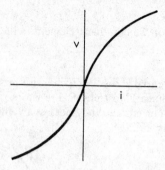

Figure 6.25   Typical iron-cored inductor characteristic

6.5.2 Analytical techniques

There are many different ways of analysing non-linear circuits but for simple non-linearities such as those discussed in the previous section approximate solutions may be obtained by using simple techniques. Examples of these are considered below.

Approximate analytical solution

If the voltage–current characteristic of a non-linear device can be described mathematically then the mathematical equation may be simplified to obtain an approximate solution. One of the most useful ways of describing non-linear characteristics is the power series

$$i = a_0 + a_1 v + a_2 v^2 + a_3 v^3 + \ldots \tag{6.81}$$

If the first two terms only are considered and powers of v higher than 1 are neglected then this is a linear approximation of the non-linear characteristic. Obviously the higher the power of v considered the more accurate in the solution but the analysis is obviously more difficult. As an example, the inductor characteristic of fig. 6.25 may be represented by

$$i = a_1 v + a_3 v^3$$

Thus if

$$v = V_m \cos \omega t$$

then

$$i = a_1 V_m \cos \omega t + a_3 V_m^3 \cos^3 \omega t$$

and

$$i = (a_1 V_m + \tfrac{3}{4} a_3 V_m^3) \cos \omega t + \tfrac{1}{4} a_3 V_m^3 \cos 3\omega t$$

Thus the response of the inductor to a sinusoidal applied voltage consists of a sinusoidal current of the same frequency as the voltage and a sinusoidal current of three times that frequency. This predicts the third-harmonic current taken by iron-cored inductors.

Piecewise linearisation

A non-linear characteristic may be represented by a collection of linear sections or 'pieces'. Thus the saturation characteristic of fig. 6.26 may be split into two sections each represented by a straight line as shown. Below the 'knee' of this typical saturation curve the characteristic is that of a linear element.

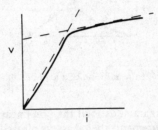

Figure 6.26   Illustration of piece-wise linearisation of a non-linear characteristic

Load line

If a circuit contains only one non-linearity, the voltage–current characteristic of which is known, then a simple but powerful technique is available based upon the load line.

Consider a resistive network containing one non-linear resistor and in which all the sources are d.c. The network may be considered as two one-port networks connected together; one of the one-port networks is the non-linear resistor and the other is the remaining, linear, network. The linear one-port network may be replaced by its Thévenin equivalent of a single voltage source and a source resistance as shown in fig. 6.27.

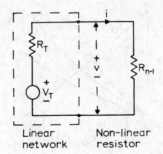

Figure 6.27   Equivalent circuit of a resistive network containing one non-linear resistor

If a given current of i amperes is supplied by the source to the load then the voltage at the terminals v is

$$v = V_T - R_T i$$

This equation of a straight line is known as the *load line* of the linear network. The load line intercepts the voltage axis at V_T (that is, when the load resistance is infinite and the current zero) and the current axis at V_T/R_T (that is, when the load resistance is zero) as shown in fig. 6.28. The slope of the load line is seen to be $-R_T$.

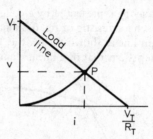

Figure 6.28   Illustration of the addition of a load-line to a non-linear characteristic

If the voltage–current characteristic of the non-linear resistance is also known, either by analysis or measurement, then it too is plotted on the voltage–current graph as shown in fig. 6.28.

In order that both voltage–current characteristics may be satisfied simultaneously the intercept of the two characteristics is the only possible condition. The point P on fig. 6.28 is known as the *operating point*.

The voltage–current characteristics of some three- or four-terminal electrical devices such as thermionic valves, transistors, amplidynes, etc. are not single curves but a family of curves. The curve which is pertinent at a given time depends upon an input variable (for example, the base current of a transistor). The operating point of such a device may also be determined by superimposing a load line on the characteristic as shown in fig. 6.29. The operating point moves as the input variable is changed.

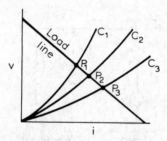

Figure 6.29   Load-line added to the characteristics of a three-terminal non-linear element

Worked example
A non-linear device has the following voltage–current characteristic.

v (V)	0	1	2	3	4	6	8	10
i (mA)	0	1.6	4	6	7.6	8.4	8.8	9.2

The voltage–current characteristic of the device is shown in fig. 6.30.

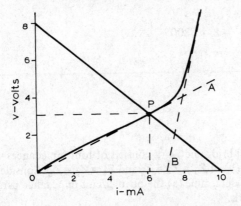

Figure 6.30   Non-linear characteristic and load-line of worked example

A piecewise linearised representation of the device is the two dotted straight lines (A and B) shown. The linearised representation is:

for $0 < i \leqslant 8mA$

line A

$$v = \frac{4}{8} \ i \ 10^3 \ \text{V}$$

for $i > 8mA$

line B

$$v = \left(\frac{8.4}{2}\right)(i - 7) \ 10^3 \ \text{V}$$

Consider that the device is connected in series with an 8 V battery and an 800 Ω resistance. The voltage–current load line of the battery–resistance combination is shown in fig. 6.30. The intercepts are

8 V

and

$$\frac{8}{800} = 10mA$$

and the slope of the line is − 800 volts/ampere.

The operating point of the circuit is at the intercept P and hence the current is 6.2mA.

Using the piecewise linearised representation, the intercept is obviously with line A. Hence

$$v = i \; \frac{4}{8} \; \times 10^3 = 8 - i \; 800$$

and hence

$$i = 6.15mA.$$

Problems

6.1   A symmetrical bridge network consists of four impedances which have values, referred to fig. 6.13(b) of $Z_1 = Z_4 = Z_a$ and $Z_2 = Z_3 = Z_b$. Considering the bridge as a two-port network determine (a) the open-circuit impedance parameters; (b) the equivalent T network.

6.2   For the bridge circuit of problem 1 determine (a) the short-circuit admittance parameters; (b) the equivalent Π network.

6.3   Construct the phasor diagram of the circuit shown in fig. 6.31. Phasors representing the quantities $i_1, i_2, v_1, v_2, i_L, i_C$ and v_L should all be shown on the diagram.

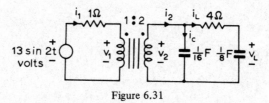

Figure 6.31

6.4   For the frequency-domain circuit of fig. 6.32, determine the source current and the voltage across the inductance. Construct the phasor diagram of the circuit.

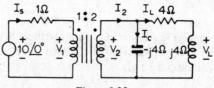

Figure 6.32

6.5   The output stage of a transistorised amplifier may be represented by a constant-current source in parallel with a 1 mS conductance. The amplifier is to be connected via an ideal transformer to a loudspeaker of 3 Ω resistance. Determine the turns ratio of the transformer in order that the loudspeaker shall absorb maximum power.

6.6   An a.c. bridge used to measure the parameters of inductors has the configuration shown in fig. 6.13 and operates at a frequency of 100 rad s⁻¹. At balance for a particular inductor the bridge parameters are: Z_1 is a resistance of 10 Ω, Z_4 is a resistance of 20 Ω, Z_3 consists of a capacitance of 2.5 mF in series with a resistance of 2 Ω and Z_2 is the unknown inductor. Determine (a) the equivalent series-connected resistance and inductance of the inductor and (b) the equivalent parallel-connected resistance and inductance of the inductor.

6.7   Each phase of a balanced, three-phase impedance consists of an inductance of 0.4 H in series with a resistance of 30 Ω. The impedance is delta-connected to a balanced, three-phase, supply of 200 V r.m.s. line-to-line and a frequency of 100 rad s^{-1}. Construct the phasor diagram of the circuit voltages and currents and determine: (a) the line currents and their phases with the line-to-line voltage V_{ab} as the reference phasor; (b) the power absorbed by the impedance.

6.8   The impedance of problem 7 is now star-connected to the supply. Construct the phasor diagram and determine: (a) the line currents and their phases with respect to the phasor V_{ab}; (b) the line-to-neutral voltages on the impedances and their phases with respect to V_{ab}; (c) the power absorbed by the impedance.

6.9   The voltage–current characteristic of a non-linear resistor (A) is as follows:

V (V)	0	0.5	1.0	1.5	2.0	2.5	3.0	3.5	4.0	4.5	5.0	5.5	6.0
I (A)	0	1.4	2.6	3.3	3.8	4.05	4.3	4.45	4.6	4.7	4.8	4.9	5.0

Determine the current through the resistor (A) when it is connected in the circuit shown in Fig. 6.33.

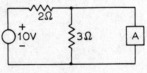

Figure 6.33

6.10   The voltage–current characteristic of a non-linear resistor (A) is as follows:

V (V)	0	2	4	6	8	10	12	14
I (A)	0	0.54	0.86	1.12	1.35	1.58	1.8	2.0

The resistor is connected in the circuit shown in fig. 6.34. Determine the voltage across the resistor (A) by the load-line method.

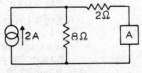

Figure 6.34

Solutions to Problems

Chapter 1

1.1 (a) $M^{-1}L^{-3}T^3I^2$; (b) $M^{-1}L^{-3}T^4I^2$;
(c) $ML^2T^{-2}I^{-1}$

1.3 (a) 102.5 W; (b) 11.8 V; (c) 5900 W;
(d) 6000 W

1.4 Two in series connected in parallel with two others. The combination connected in series with the fifth

1.5 6 V; 16 W

1.6 2 A; 32 W; 8 V

1.7 $\frac{4}{5}$ Ω; $\frac{11}{20}$ Ω

1.8 $\frac{3}{4}$ Ω; $\frac{7}{12}$ Ω

1.9 67.5 A, 82.5 A; No. 1, 237.3 V; No. 2, 236.15 V; No. 3, 235.4 V; No. 4, 235.65 V; No. 5, 236.7 V

Chapter 2

2.1 $3i_1 + 2i_2 = 0$; Constraint equation, $i_1 - i_2 = 5$; $i_1 = 2$ A; $i_2 = -3$ A

2.2 $v_a\frac{1}{3} + v_a\frac{1}{2} = -5$; $v_a = 2i_2$; $v_a = -3i_1$; $i_1 = 2$ A; $i_2 = -3$ A

2.3 $v_1 3 + v_2 2 = 0$ (from supernode 1 + 2); constraint equation $v_1 - v_2 = 5$; $v_1 = 2$ V; $v_2 = -3$ V

2.5

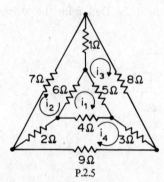

P.2.5

The network is unique

2.6

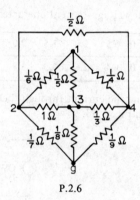

P.2.6

$$15v_1 - 6v_2 - 5v_3 - 4v_4 = 0$$
$$-6v_1 + 16v_2 - v_3 - 2v_4 = 0$$
$$-5v_1 - v_2 + 17v_3 - 3v_4 = 0$$
$$-4v_1 - 2v_2 - 3v_3 + 18v_4 = 0$$

2.7 (a) 1 V ± and 2.4 Ω; (b) 10 V ∓ and 10 Ω; (c) 12 V ± and 4 Ω

2.8 3470 W

2.9 384 000 W

2.10 (a) $\frac{2}{3}$ Ω, $18\frac{3}{8}$ W; (b) $R_a = 0$ (negative values of R_a not considered), 162 W

2.11 (a) 8 Ω; (b) $\frac{1}{8}$ W; (c) 4 Ω

2.12 $\frac{1}{2}$ Ω. By the principle of superposition if 1 A is fed into any junction and taken out at infinity then the currents in the four branches adjacent to the junction must, by symmetry, be $\frac{1}{4}$ A. Similarly, feeding in 1 A at infinity and extracting it at a junction causes currents of $\frac{1}{4}$ A in branches adjacent to the junction. If both these operations are carried out simultaneously at adjacent junctions, the current in the branch joining the junctions is $\frac{1}{2}$ A and the potential across

200

it is $\frac{1}{2}$ V. Thus 1 A is passed between junctions which have a potential difference of $\frac{1}{2}$ V and the effective resistance is $\frac{1}{2}$ Ω

2.13 $\frac{1}{3}$ Ω. By similar reasoning to the above

2.14 (a) $R_1 = R_2 = R_3 = \frac{2}{5}$ Ω.
(b) $G_1 = G_2 = G_3 = \frac{5}{6}$ S

2.15 $\frac{11}{9}$ Ω

2.16 (a) $\frac{1}{2}$ A↓ and $\frac{3}{4}$ S; (b) 4 A↓ and $\frac{1}{6}$ S;
(c) 3 A↑ and $\frac{1}{4}$ S

2.17 2.1 mA →

2.18 0.67 mA ↓

2.19 0.513 A↓

2.20 $r_{11} = \frac{39}{70}$ Ω; $r_{12} = r_{21} = \frac{2}{7}$ Ω; $r_{22} = \frac{3}{7}$ Ω;
$R_1 = \frac{19}{70}$ Ω; $R_3 = \frac{2}{7}$ Ω; $R_2 = \frac{1}{7}$ Ω

2.21 $g_{11} = \frac{30}{11}$ S; $g_{12} = g_{21} = -\frac{20}{11}$ S; $g_{22} = \frac{39}{11}$ S;
$G_1 = \frac{10}{11}$ S; $G_3 = \frac{20}{11}$ S; $G_2 = \frac{19}{11}$ S

Chapter 3

3.1 (a) $2\frac{3}{4}$ F; (b) $3\frac{1}{5}$ F; (c) $\frac{39}{40}$ F

3.2 (a) $\frac{4}{3}$ H; (b) $\frac{5}{4}$ H; (c) $\frac{40}{9}$ H

3.3 133 pF + 556 pF = 689 pF total; the same value of 689 pF

3.4 Eight possible connections: (a) coil one alone–4 H; (b) coil two alone–2 H; (c) series opposition–4 H; (d) series addition–8 H;
(e) parallel addition–$\frac{7}{4}$ H; (f) parallel reversed –$\frac{7}{8}$ H (g) coil two short-circuited–$\frac{7}{2}$ H;
(h) coil one short-circuited–$\frac{7}{4}$ H

3.5 (a) 11 H; (b) $4\frac{3}{4}$ H

3.6

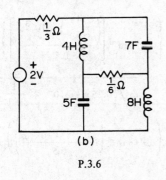

(a)

(b)

P.3.6

Chapter 4

4.1 36 J; $V_{1F} = V_{2F} = 4$ V; 24 J

4.2 At $t = 0$: $i_{c3} = i_{c5} = \frac{20}{3}$ A;
$v_{c3} = v_{c5} = 0$ V; $i_{L2} = i_{L7} = 0$; $v_{L2} = \frac{100}{3}$ V;
$v_{L7} = \frac{80}{3}$ V; at $t = \infty$: $v_{L2} = v_{L7} = i_{c3} = i_{c5} = 0$;
$i_{L2} = i_{L7} = 5$ A; $v_{c3} = 20$ V; $v_{c5} = 50$ V;

node a: $(v_a - v_b) + \frac{1}{2}\int_0^t (v_a - v_c)\,dt + \frac{1}{10}v_a = 10$;

node b: $(v_b - v_a) + 3\frac{d}{dt}(v_b - v_d) = 0$;

node c: $\frac{1}{2}\int_0^t (v_c - v_a)\,dt + \frac{1}{4}(v_c - v_d)$
$$+ 5\frac{dv_c}{dt} = 0;$$

node d: $3\frac{d}{dt}(v_d - v_b) + \frac{1}{7}\int_0^t (v_d - v_e)\,dt$
$$+ \frac{1}{4}(v_d - v_c) = 0;$$

node e: $\frac{v_e}{6} + \frac{1}{7}\int_0^t (v_e - v_d)\,dt = 0$

4.3 (a) At $t = 0$: $i_{L4} = i_{L6} = v_{c2} = v_{c3} = 0$;
$v_{L4} = 80$ V; $v_{L6} = 40$ V; $i_{c2} = i_{c3} = 4$ A;
(b) at $t = \infty$: $i_{c2} = i_{c3} = v_{L4} = v_{L6} = 0$;
$i_{L4} = i_{L6} = 5$ A; $v_{c2} = 50$ V; $v_{c3} = 75$ V;

(c) $5i_\alpha + 4\frac{d}{dt}(i_\alpha - i_\beta) + \frac{1}{3}\int_0^t (i_\alpha - i_\gamma)\,dt = 100$;

$10i_\beta + \frac{1}{2}\int_0^t (i_\beta)\,dt + 10(i_\beta - i_\gamma)$
$$+ 4\frac{d}{dt}(i_\beta - i_\alpha) = 0;$$

$10(i_\gamma - i_\beta) + 6\frac{di_\gamma}{dt} + 5i_\gamma$
$$+ \frac{1}{3}\int_0^t (i_\gamma - i_\alpha)\,dt = 0$$

4.4 Four meshes; three topological and one pseudo mesh;

mesh α: $10(i_\alpha - i_\delta) + 2\dfrac{d}{dt}(i_\alpha - i_\beta)$

$$+ \frac{1}{5}\int_0^t (i_\alpha - i_\gamma)\,dt = 0;$$

mesh β: $2\dfrac{d}{dt}(i_\beta - i_\alpha) + i_\beta + \dfrac{1}{3}\int_0^t (i_\beta - i_\gamma)\,dt$

$$+ 4(i_\beta - i_\gamma) = 0;$$

mesh γ: $\dfrac{1}{5}\int_0^t (i_\gamma - i_\alpha) \cdot dt + 4(i_\gamma - i_\beta)$

$$+ 7\frac{di_\gamma}{dt} + 6i_\gamma = 0;$$

constraint equation; $i_\delta = 10$

4.5

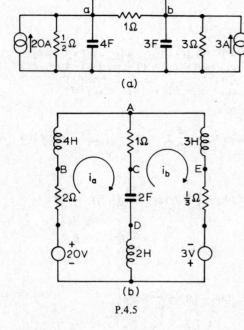

(a)

(b)

P.4.5

node A: $\dfrac{1}{4}\int_0^t (v_a - v_b)\,dt + (v_a - v_c)$

$$+ \frac{1}{3}\int_0^t (v_a - v_c)\,dt = 0;$$

node B: $\dfrac{1}{4}\int_0^t (v_b - v_a)\,dt + \dfrac{(v_b - 20)}{2} = 0;$

node C: $(v_c - v_a) + 2\dfrac{d}{dt}(v_c - v_d) = 0;$

node D: $2\dfrac{d}{dt}(v_d - v_c) + \dfrac{1}{2}\int_0^t v_d\,dt = 0;$

node E: $\dfrac{1}{3}\int_0^t (v_e - v_a)\,dt + (v_e + 3)3 = 0$

4.6 $v_{c1} = 4(1 - e^{-t3/8})$; 36 J; 24 J; 12 J

4.7 (a) $v = 4(1 - e^{-t/4})$; (b) $v = 4\,e^{-t}$

4.8 (a) 0; (b) 8 V; (c) $i = 1.6\,e^{-t/6}$; (d) 3.2 V

4.9 (a) for $0 \leqslant t \leqslant 1\ v = 5\,(1 - e^{-2t})$; for $t \geqslant 1\ v = 4.32\,e^{-2(t-1)}$; (b) 4.32 V; 0.588 V; $4.32 \times e^{-18}$ V $\simeq 0$

4.10 (a) $v = 6(1 - e^{-t/3})$; (b) $v = 8(1 - e^{-t/4})$

4.11 (a) $i = 2(e^{-t/4} - e^{-t/2})$; (b) 2.77 s; (c) 0.5 A; (d) 1 F

4.12 (a) 0; (b) 0; (c) 0.5 V; (d) $v_{ba} = 2(e^{-t/2} - e^{-t})$

4.13 $v = 3 + e^{-t/5}$

4.14 (a) $v = 1.03\,e^{-t/4}\sin(0.97t)$; (b) 2; (c) 4 S;

4.15 $i_1 = 6t + 0.6(1 - e^{-2t})$; $i_2 = 1.2(1 - e^{-2t})$; at $t = 0$; $i_1 = i_2 = 0$; at $t = \infty$; $i_2 = 1.2$, $i_1 = \infty$

Chapter 5

5.1 (a) $v = \dfrac{1}{\sqrt{\left\{0.25 + \left(\omega 10^{-3} - \dfrac{1}{\omega 10^{-3}}\right)^2\right\}}}$

$$\times \sin\left\{\omega t + \tan^{-1}\left[\frac{\left[\dfrac{1}{\omega 10^{-3}}\right] - 10^{-3}\omega}{0.5}\right]\right\}$$

(b) $i_L = -\dfrac{1}{\omega\sqrt{\left\{0.25 + \left(\omega 10^{-3} - \dfrac{1}{\omega 10^{-3}}\right)^2\right\}}}$

$$\times \cos\left(\omega t + \tan^{-1}\left\{\frac{\dfrac{1}{\omega 10^{-3}} - 10^{-3}\omega}{0.5}\right\}\right)$$

(d) $\omega_0 = 1000$ rad s^{-1}; $Q = 2$; $B = 500$ rad s^{-1}.
For $i_L = 0.707(i_L)_{max}$, $\omega = 1167$ or
625 rad s^{-1}

5.3 $\quad \omega = 4640$ rad s^{-1} and $I_{L(max)} = 1.75 I_s$

5.4 (a) 8 W; 0.895; 1.414 A; 6.32 V;
(b) 25 mW; 0.707; 5 mA; 7.07 V; (c) 5 mW;
1; 70.7 μA; 70.7 V

5.5 (a) 0 V mean; 7.07 V r.m.s.; (b) 0 V
mean; 5.78 V r.m.s.; (c) 0 V mean; 10 V r.m.s.;
(d) 3.19 V mean; 5 V r.m.s.; (e) 6.38 V mean;
7.07 V r.m.s.

5.6 $\quad I_G = 1 \angle 0$; $I_L = 1.59 \angle -90°$;
$I_C = 3.14 \angle +90°$; $I = 1.85 \angle 57.2°$

5.7 (a) $Z = 30 - \text{j}31.8 = 43.8 \angle -47°$;
$Y = 0.015 + \text{j}0.016 = 0.022 \angle +47°$
(b) $Z = 15.6 + \text{j}15.1 = 21.7 \angle +44°$;
$Y = 0.033 - \text{j}0.0318 = 0.046 \angle -44°$
(c) $Z = 30 - \text{j}0.4 = 30 \angle -46'$;
$Y = 0.033 + \text{j}0.0004 = 0.033 \angle +46'$
(d) $Z = 30 + \text{j}0.4 = 30 \angle +46'$;
$Y = 0.033 - \text{j}0.0004 = 0.033 \angle -46'$

5.8 (a) $16000 \angle 51.6°$; (b) $85 \angle -32°$;
(c) $21.6 \angle -90°$

5.9 (a) $Y = 0.25 \angle +2°$; $G = 0.25$ S;
$B = +0.0097$ S; (b) $Y = 0.2 \angle -36.8°$;
$G = 0.16$ S; $B = -0.12$ S

5.10 (a) $30 \sin (2t + 0.927)$; (b) $30 \sin$
$(2t - 0.927)$; (c) $36 \sin 2t$; (d) $25 \sin 2t$

5.11 (a) $5 \angle 53.1°$; (b) $2.83 \angle 45°$; (c) $4 \angle 0°$

5.12 (a) 0; (b) 50 rad s^{-1}

5.13 (a) $0.412 \times 10^{-3} \angle 19.8°$;
(b) $4.25 \times 10^{-3} \angle 64.8°$

5.14 4472 VA; 4000 W; +2000 VAr

5.15 (a) 89.44 VA; 80 W; -40 VAr;
(b) 231 VA; 192.3 W; -128.2 VAr

5.16 (a) 638 VA; 625 W; -125 VAr;
(b) 10 000 VA; 8000 W; -6000 VAr

5.17 (a) 5 mH; (b) 20 Ω and 5 mH;
(c) 10.6 Ω

5.18 $\quad G = 1.72$ S; $C = 6.9$ mF; 0.25 W

5.19 $\quad i_L = 2.5 \sin \left(2t - \dfrac{\pi}{2} \right)$; $P = 9\frac{3}{8}$ W

5.20 0.414 W

Chapter 6

6.1 (a) $z_{11} = z_{22} = \frac{1}{2}(Z_a + Z_b)$;
$z_{12} = z_{21} = \frac{1}{2}(Z_b - Z_a)$;
(b) $Z_1 = Z_2 = Z_a$; $Z_3 = \frac{1}{2}(Z_b - Z_a)$

6.2 (a) $y_{11} = y_{22} = \dfrac{1}{2}\left(\dfrac{1}{Z_a} + \dfrac{1}{Z_b} \right)$;
$y_{12} = y_{21} = \dfrac{1}{2}\left(\dfrac{1}{Z_b} - \dfrac{1}{Z_a} \right)$;

(b) $Y_1 = Y_2 = \dfrac{1}{Z_b}$; $Y_3 = \dfrac{1}{2}\left(\dfrac{1}{Z_a} - \dfrac{1}{Z_b} \right)$.

6.3 The amplitude phasors are: $I_1 = 7 + \text{j}4$;
$I_2 = 3.5 + \text{j}2$; $I_C = 1 + \text{j}1.5$; $I_L = 2.5 + \text{j}0.5$;
$V_1 = 6 - \text{j}4$; $V_2 = 12 - \text{j}8$; $V_L = 2 - \text{j}10$.

6.4 $\quad I_S = 4 + \text{j}2$; $V_L = 8 + \text{j}4$; the amplitude
phasors are $V_1 = 6 - \text{j}2$, $V_2 = 12 - \text{j}4$,
$V_L = 8 + \text{j}4$, $I_S = 4 + \text{j}2$, $I_2 = 2 + \text{j}1$,
$I_C = 1 + \text{j}3$, $I_L = 1 - \text{j}2$.

6.5 18.3:1

6.6 (a) $R_s = 20$ Ω; $L_s = 0.4$ H; (b) $R_p = 100$ Ω;
$L_p = 0.5$ H.

6.7 (a) $I_a = 6.93 \angle -83.2°$; $I_b = 6.93 \angle 203.2°$;
$I_C = 6.93 \angle -323.2°$; (b) $P = 1440$ W

6.8 (a) $I_a = 2.31 \angle -83.2°$; $I_b = 2.31 \angle 203.2°$;
$I_c = 2.31 \angle -323.2°$; (b) $V_{an} = 115.5 \angle -30°$;
$V_{bn} = 115.5 \angle -150°$; $V_{cn} = 115.5 \angle -270°$;
(c) 480 W

6.9 3.55 A

6.10 5.5 V

Index